HAZARDOUS MATERIALS FOR FIRST RESPONDERS COURSE WORKBOOK

Instructional Developer

Andrea Haken

Editor

Melissa Noakes

Based on the Manual
validated by the International Fire
Service Training Association

Published by
Fire Protection Publications
Oklahoma State University

RECYCLABLE

Table of Contents

How to Use this Workbook

The **Hazardous Materials For First Responders Workbook** accompanies the fourth edition of the IFSTA **Hazardous Materials For First Responders** manual.

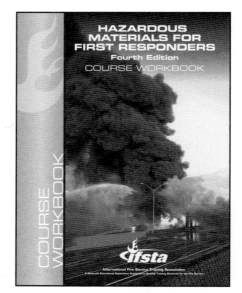

This workbook is designed to work in a number of ways. The workbook can be used as a study guide for self-study. Although the answers are not included in this book, the page numbers are included that reference the manual pages on which the answers can be found. The workbook may also be used as a homework assignment given by your instructor. In either case, the best approach to using this workbook is to read the questions through in their entirety, answer those questions that you can answer on your own, and look up those questions that you cannot answer in the manual.

The answers to the questions in this workbook can be found on the **Hazardous Materials For First Responders fourth edition Curriculum CD**. If portions of this workbook are assigned as homework, your instructor will have access to these answers.

If you have any questions about this product or any of the **Hazardous Materials For First Responders fourth edition** family of products, call Fire Protection Publications at 800.654.4055 or visit our website at **www. IFSTA.org**.

Chapter 1

Introduction to Hazardous Materials

Terms

Write the definition of the terms below on the blanks provided.

1. Hazardous Material (9) _US posses an unreasonble risk to health and Safety_

2. Dangerous Goods (9) _U.N. Classification of Hazmat_

3. Weapon of Mass Destruction (WMD) (10) _Weapon intended on causing death or serious bodily harm_

4. Personal Protective Equipment (PPE) (10) _Safety equip worn_

5. Environmental Protection Agency (EPA) (11) _US. gov. Agency, Creates & enforces laws to protect environment_

6. Occupational Safety and Health Administration (OSHA) (11) _U.S. Federal agency develops and enforces safety in the workplace_

7. Hazardous Waste Operations and Emergency Response (HAZWOPER) (11) _U.S. regs in Title 29 (labor) CFR 1910.120, emergency response cleanup_

8. Authority Having Jurisdiction (AHJ) (12) _legal entity has statutory authority to enforce codet approve equip_

9. National Fire Protection Association (NFPA®) (12) _US non-profit org. Quincy, Mass. Sets standards & educates_

10. Standard Operating Procedures (SOPs) (12) Standard methods a dept. uses to carry out routine functions

11. Awareness Level (13) 1st level of training in hazmat defensive NFPA 472 & OSHA 29 CFR 1910.120

12. Operations Level (13) 2nd level of training Offensive OPS (Tech., Branch O., Branch Safety O, Branch I.C., Private Sector.

13. Mitigate (15) less harsh, actions to reduce

14. Acute (15) Rapid onset

15. Acute Health Effects (15) Health effects w/rapid onset

16. Chronic (15) long duration, overtime

17. Chronic Health Effects (15) long term health effects

18. Hazard (15) Component that can cause injury or loss

19. Oxidation (16) rust on metal Chemical process that happens w/ O_2

20. Polymerization (16) poss. violent reaction two or more molecules combine to form larger one

21. Cryogen (16) Gas cooled to low temp. -130 F/-90 C Changes to a liquid.

Flounder
Flourine

22. Corrosive Material (16) Gaseous, liquid, or solid that can burn tissue and corrode other materials

23. Oxidizer (16) Substance that yeilds O^2 may stimulate combustion

24. Poison (16) injurious to body + health

25. Elevated Temperature Material (17) Transported in elevated temp + $212°/100°$, above Flash phase $100F°/3F°$, Solid phase $464F/24Q$

26. Ionizing Radiation (18) Sufficient radiation to remove electrons from atoms changing Chem Comp Alpha, Beta, Gamma, neutron

27. Nonionizing Radiation (18) Energy waves composed of oscillating electric + magnetic feilds @ Speed of light

28. Electron (20) part of an atom, Negatively charged

29. Photon (20) electromagnetic energy.

30. Contaminant (21) impurity w/ mix of forgein substance

31. Contamination (21) ''

32. Exposure (21) Contact w/ a substance

33. Asphyxiant (23) prevents O^2 from combining w/ blood

34. Systemic Effect (24) _Entire System_

35. Acid (25) _Hydrogen Containing Compound w/ water produces hydrogen ions pH-7_

36. pH (25) _Measure of acidity_

37. Ion (25) _lost or gained an electron has a pos or neg charge._

38. Base (26) _Corrosive water soluble compound an alkaline caustic substance. hydroxide ions in water_

39. Irritant/Irritating Material (27) _liquid/solid, fire or air presents dangerous fumes_

40. Convulsant (27) _poison that causes exposed individual to seizure_

41. Carcinogen (27) _Cancer producing substance._

42. Allergen (28) _Material that can cause an allergic reaction._

43. Infectious (30) _transmittable_

44. Contagious (30) _Person to person to transmission_

45. Improvised Explosive Device (IED) (31) _____

46. Reactivity/Instability (31) _ability of two or more Chem. mixed together to cause an energistic release_

47. Routes of Entry (32) _pathways by which hazards enter the body_

48. Comprehensive Environmental Response, Compensation, and Liability Act (CERCLA) (34) _U.S. law to tax Chem + Petrol ind. + provide Fed authority_

49. Local Emergency Planning Committee (LEPC) (40) _individuals from local offices, Citizens and ind. reps responsible for emergency planning_

50. Hazardous Wastes (51) _discarded materials regulated by the EPA because of environmental Concerns_

51. Agency for Toxic Substances and Disease Registry (ATSDR) (53) _lead U.S. phA. responsible for implementing Car + registry_

Matching

Write the correct effective characteristic on the blanks provided.

 _A_ 1. Identify actions to protect themselves and others from hazards (13-14)

 _B_ 2. Identify the hazardous material(s) involved in an incident if possible (14-15)

 _A_ 3. Recognize the presence or potential presence of a hazardous material (13-14)

 _B_ 4. Analyze an incident to determine the nature and extent of the problem (14-15)

 _A_ 5. Establish scene control by isolating the hazardous area and denying entry (13-14)

A. Awareness-Level Personnel

B. Operations-Level Personnel

_A_ 6. Recognize the type of container at a site and identify the material in it if possible (13-14)

_A_ 7. Transmit information to an appropriate authority and call for appropriate assistance (13-14)

_B_ 8. Evaluate the progress of the actions taken to ensure that response objectives are safely met (14-15)

_B_ 9. Protect themselves, nearby persons, the environment, and property from the effects of a release (14-15)

_B_ 10. Develop a defensive plan of action to address the problems presented by the incident (plan a response) (14-15)

_B_ 11. Implement the planned response to control a release from a safe distance and keep it from spreading (14-15)

A. Awareness-Level Personnel
B. Operations-Level Personnel

True/False

Write True or False on the blanks provided; if False, write the correct statement on the lines provided.

_T_ 1. A hazardous materials incident is an emergency involving a substance that poses an unreasonable risk to people, the environment, or property. (9)

_____

_____

_T_ 2. First responders must know their limitations and realize when they cannot proceed any farther. (11)

_____

_____

_F_ 3. In Canada, the maximum acceptable level of training for first responders is NFPA® 472. (12)

_Minimum level_____

_____

_____ T   4. OSHA considers personnel trained to each level (Awareness and Operations) to be first responders. (13)

_____

_____

_____ T   5. It is important to monitor for radiation at any incident involving explosions or suspected terrorist attacks. (22)

_____

_____

_____ T   6. Many toxins (poisons) have slow-acting, acute toxic effects while others may have chronic effects that are not manifested for many years. (24)

_____

_____

_____ T   7. Hydrogen peroxide is a corrosive that is neither an acid nor a base. (25)

_____

_____

_____ T   8. First responders should keep in mind that chronic health effects of substances may not be known for many years, and what is considered safe today, may not be tomorrow. (28)

_____

_____

_____   9. State Emergency Response Commissions (SERC) are required to divide their states into Emergency Planning Districts and to name a District Emergency Planning Committee (DEPC) for each district. (40)

_____

_____

_____   10. The Bureau of Alcohol, Tobacco, Firearms, and Explosives (ATF) is an agency involved with hazardous materials. (43)

_____

_____

_____   11. The United States Nuclear Safety Commission can be best described as the watchdog over the use of nuclear energy and materials in Canada. (47)

_____

_____

1

Short Answer

Write the correct answers on the blanks provided.

1. What are the causes for incidents involving hazardous materials? (10)

_____

_____

_____

_____

_____

2. List four of the mission-specific competencies identified in NFPA® 472. (13)

_____

_____

_____

_____

3. List three hazards that have the potential to cause harm (acute/chronic effects) at hazardous materials incidents. (16)

_____

_____

_____

4. Why must any clothing saturated with cryogenic material be removed? (16-17)

_____

_____

_____

5. List four biological/etiological hazards. (29-30)

_____

_____

_____

_____

6. List the five routes of entry. (32-33)

_____

_____

7. What are the four main agencies involved in the regulation of hazardous materials and/or wastes in the U.S.? (38)

_____

_____

_____

_____

8. Records have shown that the majority of haz mat incidents involve what products? (51)

_____

_____

_____

_____

Multiple Choice

Write the correct answers on the blanks provided.

_____ 1. Which of the following is NOT a level above the Operations Level for OSHA? (13)
   A. Hazardous Materials Technician
   B. Hazardous Materials Specialist
   C. On Scene Incident Commander
   D. Private Sector Specialist Employee

_____ 2. A liquefied gas is one that at the charging pressure is partially liquid at: (16)
   A. 50°F (10°C).
   B. 60°F (16°C).
   C. 70°F (21°C).
   D. 80°F (27°C).

_____ 3. Which of the following is MOST difficult to measure in the field and is estimated? (21)

    A. Beta

    B. Alpha

    C. Gamma

    D. Neutron

_____ 4. What asphyxiants are gases that displace the oxygen necessary for breathing? (23)

    A. Simple

    B. Complex

    C. Chemical

    D. Radiological

_____ 5. Substances that affect the oxygenation of the body and generally lead to suffocation are: (23)

    A. poisons.

    B. allergens.

    C. carcinogens.

    D. asphyxiants.

_____ 6. Toxins that cause temporary but sometimes severe inflammation to the eyes, skin, or respiratory system are: (27)

    A. acids.

    B. irritants.

    C. convulsants.

    D. carcinogens.

_____ 7. Polyvinyl chloride, benzene, asbestos, some chlorinated hydrocarbons, arsenic, and nickel are examples of: (27)

    A. acids.

    B. irritants.

    C. convulsants.

    D. carcinogens.

_____ 8. The 2001 anthrax attack in the United States was an example of a(n) _____ attack. (31)

    A. biological

    B. mechanical

    C. asphyxiant

    D. systemic effect

9. Which of the following can be caused by an explosion? (32)
   A. Reactivity
   B. Etiological hazard
   C. Infectious disease
   D. Incendiary thermal effect

10. Which of the following can NOT be caused by toluene (solvent)? (33)
    A. Arthritis
    B. Dizziness
    C. Skin irritation
    D. Lack of coordination

11. Which of the following is the U.S. law that created a tax on chemical and petroleum industries? (34)
    A. EPA
    B. OSHA
    C. SARA
    D. CERCLA

12. The NFPA® standards on chemical protective clothing address hazards of flash fires and required garments due to event that occurred at: (38)
    A. Shreveport, LA (1984).
    B. Kansas City, MO (1988).
    C. Love Canal, Niagara Falls (1978).
    D. Torrey Canyon tank ship, England and France (1967).

13. CERCLA was responsible for all the of the following EXCEPT: (39-40)
    A. Superfund actions to consider the standards and requirements found in other state and federal environmental laws and regulations.
    B. Establishing prohibitions and requirements concerning closed and abandoned hazardous waste sites.
    C. Providing for liability of persons responsible for releases of hazardous waste at these sites.
    D. Establishing a trust fund to provide for cleanup when no responsible party could be identified.

14. The Local Emergency Planning Committee (LEPC) was required by which of the following to be composed of local officials, citizens, and industry representatives? (40)
    A. TSCA 1976
    B. RCRA 1986
    C. Title 29 CFR
    D. Title III of SARA

15. The Nuclear Regulatory Commission (NRC) regulates U.S. commercial nuclear power plants and the civilian use of nuclear materials as well as the possession, use, storage, and transfer of radioactive materials through: (42)

   A. Title 10 CFR 10.
   B. Title 10 CFR 20.
   C. Title 29 CFR 10.
   D. Title 29 CFR 20.

16. If xylene were marketed to consumers for purchase and use, it would fall subject to the Consumer Product Safety Commission, and be called a hazardous: (51)

   A. waste.
   B. material.
   C. chemical.
   D. substance.

17. Which of the following is responsible for publishing and maintaining the official Mexican standards (NOMs) covering the Mexican Hazardous Materials Land Transportation Regulation? (47)

   A. The Ministry of Labor and Social Welfare (Secretaría del Trabajo y Previsión Social) (STPS)
   B. Federal Telecommunications Commission (Comisión Federal de Telecomunicaciones) (CFT)
   C. The Ministry of Communications and Transport (Secretaría de Comunicaciones y Transportes) (SCT)
   D. The Ministry of Environment and Natural Resources (Secretaría de Medio Ambiente y Recursos Naturales) (SEMARNAT)

18. Which of the following has a main purpose of creating a state environmental protection policy and overseeing the Federal General Law of Ecological Equilibrium and the Protection of the Environment (LGEEPA)? (50)

   A. The Ministry of Labor and Social Welfare (Secretaría del Trabajo y Previsión Social) (STPS)
   B. Federal Telecommunications Commission (Comisión Federal de Telecomunicaciones) (CFT)
   C. The Ministry of Communications and Transport (Secretaría de Comunicaciones y Transportes) (SCT)
   D. The Ministry of Environment and Natural Resources (Secretaría de Medio Ambiente y Recursos Naturales) (SEMARNAT)

Crossword

Across

3 General term for the equipment worn by fire and emergency services responders.

6 Level of training established by OSHA allowing first responders to take defensive actions at hazardous materials incidents.

10 Any foreign substance that compromises the purity of a given substance.

11 Reactions in which two or more molecules chemically combine to form larger molecules.

13 Condition of impurity resulting from a mixture or contact with foreign substance.

16 Transmittable, able to infect people.

19 Minute component of an atom that possesses a negative charge.

21 Term used in codes and standards to identify the legal entity.

23 Condition, substance, or device that can directly cause injury or loss; the source of a risk.

26 To cause to become less harsh or hostile; to make less severe, intense or painful.

27 Material that when offered for transportation in bulk packaging is in a liquid phase and at a temperature at or above 212°F (100°C).

30 Contact with a substance by swallowing, breathing, or touching the skin or eyes.

31 Pathways by which hazardous materials get into (or affect) the human body.

Down

1 Liquid or solid that upon contact with fire or exposure to air emits dangerous fumes.

2 Any device that is intended to cause death to a significant number of people.

4 Government agency that creates laws to protect the air, water, and soil from contamination.

5 Standard methods in which a fire department operates to carry out a routine function.

7 Series of energy waves composed of oscillating electric and magnetic fields.

8 Something that affects an entire system rather than a single location or entity.

9 Cancer-producing substance.

10 Long duration, or recurring over a period of time.

12 Chemical process that occurs when a substance combines with oxygen.

14 Characterized by having rapid onset and a relatively short duration.

15 Gas that is cooled to low temperature, usually below -130°F (-90°C), to change to a liquid.

17 Any substance or material that yields oxygen.

18 Gaseous, liquid, or solid material that can destroy human skin tissue.

20 Lowest level of training established by OSHA for personnel at hazardous materials incidents.

22 Corrosive water-soluble compound.

24 Poison that causes an exposed individual to have convulsions.

25 Material that can cause an allergic reaction of the skin or respiratory system.

28 Any material that when taken into the body is injurious to health.

29 Compound containing hydrogen that reacts with water to produce hydrogen ions.

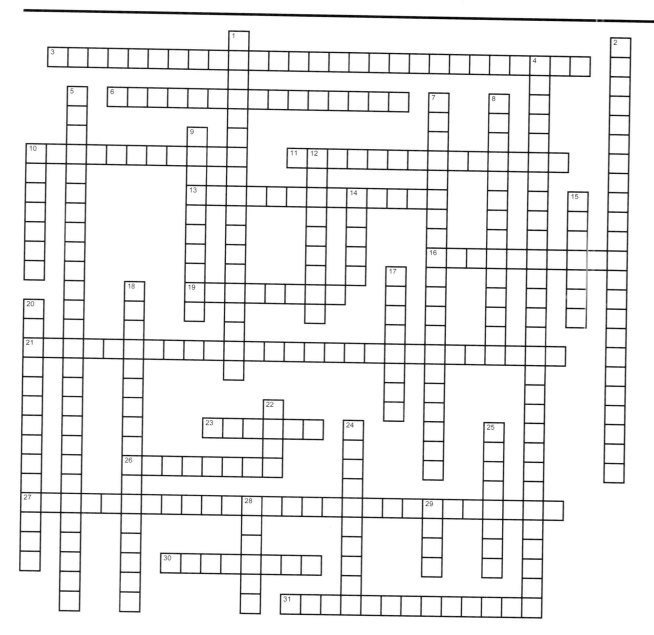

Chapter 2

Hazardous Materials Identification

Terms

Write the definition of the terms below on the blanks provided.

1. Pre-Incident Survey (66) _____

   _____

2. Occupancy (66) _____

   _____

3. Terrorism (71) _____

   _____

4. Packaging (71) _____

   _____

5. Bulk Packaging (72) _____

   _____

6. Nonbulk Packaging (72) _____

   _____

7. Cryogenic Liquid Storage Tank (73) _____

   _____

8. Intermodal Container (77) _____

   _____

9. Manway (80) _____

   _____

10. Ring Stiffener (84) _____

_____

11. Refrigerated Intermodal Container (92) _____

_____

12. Reporting Marks (130) _____

_____

13. Capacity Stencil (131) _____

_____

14. Specification Marking (131) _____

_____

15. Safety Data Sheet (135) _____

_____

16. Signal Word (137) _____

_____

17. CAS® Number (138) _____

_____

18. Bill of Lading (144) _____

_____

19. Olfactory Fatigue (150) _____

_____

20. Exothermic (152) _____

_____

21. Endothermic (152) _____

_____

22. Chemical Warfare Agent (154) _____

_____

23 Toxic Industrial Material (TIM)/Toxic Industrial Chemical (TIC) (154) _____

_____

24. Bacteria (156) _____

_____

25. Virus (156) _____

_____

26. Rickettsia (156) _____

_____

27. Biological Toxin (156) _____

_____

28. Syndromic Surveillance (156) _____

_____

29. Radiological Dispersal Device (RDD) (157) _____

_____

30. Illicit (159) _____

_____

31. Meth Lab (159) _____

_____

32. Agar (160) _____

_____

33. Secondary Device (161) _____

_____

2

Write True or False on the blanks provided; if False, write the correct statement on the lines provided.

_____   1. First responders can reduce the number of on-site decisions by conducting pre-incident surveys. (66)

_____

_____

_____   2. Paint supply stores, dry cleaners, and print shops are examples of low probable locations for hazardous materials. (66-67)

_____

_____

_____   3. Shell-to-bottom seam failures are more common among old storage tanks. (74)

_____

_____

_____   4. Steel storage tanks built before 1960 generally do not conform to current industry standards for explosion and fire venting situations. (74)

_____

_____

_____   5. The United Nations four-digit identification numbers are only used in the United States. (107)

_____

_____

_____   6. Doubling a hazard identification number indicates an intensification of that particular hazard. (109)

_____

_____

_____   7. Transborder shipments between the U.S. and Mexico are accompanied by shipping documents in both English and Spanish. (146)

_____

_____

8. Hearing is the safest of the five senses to use in the detection of a hazardous material. (150)

_____

9. Monitoring and detection devices can be used to determine the scope of the incident. (152)

_____

Identification

Identify the following items on the lines provided. (71-105)

Courtesy of Rich Mahaney

1. _____

Courtesy of Rich Mahaney

2. _____

Courtesy of Rich Mahaney

3. _____

Courtesy of Rich Mahaney

4. _____

Courtesy of Rich Mahaney

5. _____

Courtesy of Rich Mahaney

6. _____

Courtesy of Rich Mahaney

7. _____

Courtesy of Rich Mahaney

8. _____

Identification

Identify the following items on the lines provided. (78-93)

Courtesy of Rich Mahaney

1. _____

Courtesy of Rich Mahaney

2. _____

3. _____

Courtesy of Rich Mahaney

4. _____

Courtesy of Tom Clawson

5. _____

2

Short Answer

Write the correct answers on the blanks provided.

1. List the seven clues to the presence of hazardous materials. (64)

   _____

   _____

   _____

   _____

2. What are the examples of potential terrorist targets? (70-71)

   _____

   _____

   _____

   _____

   _____

   _____

   _____

3. List the types of containers for radioactive materials. (104-105)

   _____

   _____

   _____

   _____

   _____

4. What are the four signal words to indicate the degree of hazard with a product? (137)

   _____

   _____

5. List symptoms of chemical exposure. (152)

   _____

   _____

   _____

_____

_____

_____

_____

_____

6. Describe the guidelines for protecting against possible secondary devices. (161-162)

_____

_____

_____

_____

_____

Multiple Choice

Write the correct answers on the blanks provided.

_____   1. Awareness-Level personnel and first responders must be able to _____ and identify the presence of hazardous materials. (64)
    A. taste
    B. learn
    C. smell
    D. detect

_____   2. Pre-incident surveys identify all the following EXCEPT: (66)
    A. exposures.
    B. liquid testing.
    C. site characteristics.
    D. dangers of hazardous materials.

_____   3. Which of the following statements regarding water levels is LEAST accurate? (69)
    A. Tidal and flow conditions are constantly changing.
    B. Liquid levels are difficult to measure and should be estimated.
    C. Many accidents occur because flow volume and tidal conditions were not considered.
    D. Once a material reaches an outside water source, it becomes a moving incident and is extremely difficult to contain.

_____ 4. What is the unlawful use of force or violence against persons or property for the purpose of intimidating or coercing a government? (71)
   A. Terrorism
   B. Occupancy
   C. Contamination
   D. Specification Marking

_____ 5. Which of the following is NOT criteria to be considered bulk packaging? (72)
   A. Pressures between 0.5 psi (3.5 kpa) to 15 psi (103 kpa)
   B. Water capacity is 1,001 pounds (454 kg) or greater as a receptacle for a gas
   C. Maximum capacity is greater than 119 gallons (450 L) as a receptacle for a liquid
   D. Maximum net mass is greater than 882 pounds (400 kg) or maximum capacity is greater than 119 gallons (450 L) as a receptacle for a solid

_____ 6. Which of the following are cylindrical with rounded ends (heads) and have at least one manway for access to the tank's interior? (80)
   A. Bulk carrier
   B. Freight container
   C. Low-pressure tank car
   D. Intermodal container

_____ 7. Petroleum carriers are an example of a(an): (96-97)
   A. cargo tank.
   B. intermodal container.
   C. vessel cargo carrier.
   D. nit loading device.

_____ 8. What are stenciled on both sides (to the left when facing the side of the car) and both ends (upper center) of the tank car tank? (130)
   A. Placard
   B. Signal word
   C. Reporting marks
   D. Specification marking

_____ 9. The NFPA® 704 system is designed to alert emergency responders to: (133)
   A. flammability.
   B. transportation.
   C. weather conditions.
   D. chronic health hazards.

_____ 10. Which of the following is NOT an example of Globally Harmonized System of Classification and Labeling of Chemicals (GHS)? (139)

    A. Sizes

    B. Symbols

    C. Signal words

    D. Hazard statements

_____ 11. What color of the ANSI safety code means warning? (144)

    A. Red

    B. Green

    C. Yellow

    D. Orange

_____ 12. The _____ is primarily a guide to aid emergency responders in quickly identifying the specific or generic hazards of materials involved in an emergency incident and protecting themselves. (149)

    A. CIL

    B. ERG

    C. SDS

    D. MSDS

2

Across

1 Microscopic, single-celled organisms.

2 Unlawful use of force or violence against persons or property for the purpose of intimidating or coercing a government.

4 Heavily insulated, vacuum-jacketed tanks used to store cryogenic liquids, equipped with safety-relief valves and rupture disks.

7 Gradual inability of a person to detect odors after initial exposure.

8 Government-mandated warnings provided on product labels that indicate the level of toxicity.

11 Term used by the U.S. Department of Transportation to describe shipping containers and their markings, labels, and/or placards.

12 Bomb placed at the scene of an ongoing emergency response that is intended to cause casualties among responders.

15 Shipping paper used by the trucking industry indicating origin, destination, route, and product.

16 Stencil on the exterior of tank cars indicating the standards to which the tank car was built.

20 Freight container designed to be used interchangeably in two or more modes of transport.

23 General fire service term for a building, structure, or residency.

24 Unique number assigned to a chemical substance or biological sequence by the American Chemical Society's Chemical Abstract Service® registry.

26 Circumferential tank shell stiffener that helps to maintain the tank's cross section.

27 Illegal, unlawful.

28 Number stenciled on the exterior of tank cars to indicated the volume of the tank.

Down

1 Poison produced by living organisms.

3 Device that spreads radioactive contamination over the widest possible area.

5 Industrial chemical that is toxic at certain concentration.

6 Chemical substance that is intended for use in warfare or terrorist activities to kill or seriously injure people.

9 Survey of a facility or location made before an emergency occurs in order to prepare for an appropriate emergency response.

10 A sixteen-section information sheet provided by a chemical product's manufacturer or importer that contains information.

12 Surveillance using health-related data that precede diagnosis and signal a sufficient probability of a case to warrant further public health response.

13 Gelatinous or jelly-like substance used to grow bacterial cultures.

14 Chemical reaction involving the absorption of heat energy.

17 Chemical reaction between two or more materials that changes the materials and produces heat, flames, and toxic smoke.

18 Hole through which a person may go to gain access to an underground or enclosed structure.

19 Combination of letters and numbers stenciled on rail tank cars that may be used to get information about the car's contents.

21 Specialized bacteria that live and multiply in the gastrointestinal tract of arthropod carriers.

22 Simplest type of microorganism that can only replicate itself in the living cells of their hosts.

25 Illegal clandestine laboratory established to produce illegal methamphetamine (meth).

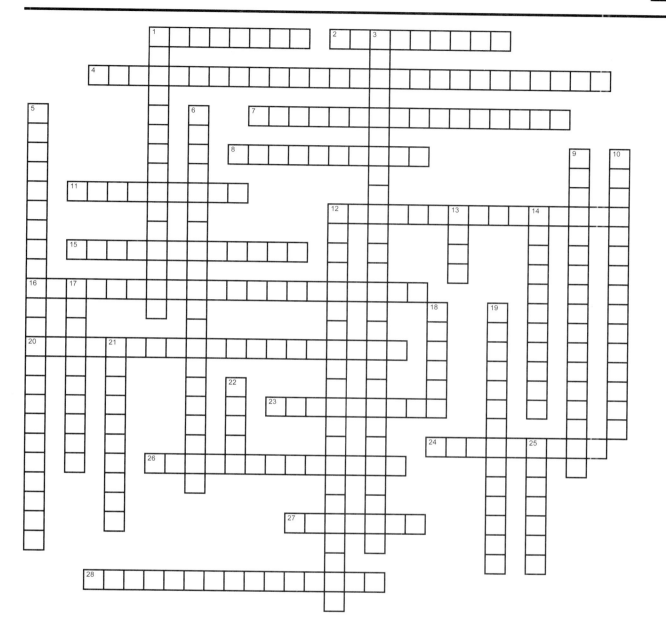

2

Learning Activity 2-1
Analyze Scenarios to Detect the Presence of Hazardous Materials

Name _____ Date _____

References

Hazardous Materials for First Responders, 4th Edition, pp. 64-167

NFPA® 472, 4.2.1, 5.2.1

Introduction

First responders do not always know the details and risks involved in an emergency response. First responders must be able to quickly determine if there is a possibility of hazardous materials at the incident. The actions that are taken when first responding to an incident help determine the success of the response. First responders must be alert for clues that may indicate hazardous materials. Clues may be obvious, such as placards or signs, or may be more subtle, such as the type of occupancy.

Read the scenarios given below and answer the questions that follow.

Activity

1. You are responding to reports of a fire at an industrial plant. Upon arrival you notice that there is an NFPA® 704 diamond on the outside of the building. The diamond is shown below:

    What is the risk of hazardous materials being present at this incident? What information does the NFPA® diamond give first responders?

    _____

    _____

    _____

    _____

2. You are responding to reports of a fire in a commercial building. The building does not have any indicators of hazardous materials on the outside. The entrance sign for the building lists several medical practices as occupants. Does this incident have any risk of hazardous materials? Why or why not?

_____

_____

_____

_____

3. You are responding to a motor vehicle accident on an overpass. Upon arrival a cargo tank truck has overturned. There are three additional cars involved in the accident and the scene is very chaotic. You notice that there is a DOT placard on the tank truck. Because of the chaos surrounding the scene you can only determine that the placard is yellow and has numbers on it. Does this incident have any risk of hazardous materials? Why or why not?

_____

_____

_____

_____

4. You are responding to reports of an accident. Workers were repairing a pipeline and one worker was involved in an equipment accident while repairing the pipeline. You do not notice any markers or color codes on or near the pipeline. What is the risk of hazardous materials at this incident? How could you find out more information about what is in the pipeline?

_____

_____

_____

_____

2

Learning Activity 2-2
Interpret Representative
Shipping Papers

Name _____ **Date** _____

References

Hazardous Materials for First Responders, 4th Edition, pp. 144-147

NFPA® 472, 4.2.1(10)

Introduction

Shipments of hazardous materials must be accompanied by shipping papers that describe the hazardous material. The information can be provided on a bill of lading, waybill, or similar document. When first responders know that a close approach to an incident is safe, they can then examine the cargo shipping papers. It is important that first responders be able to read shipping papers in order to identify the hazardous materials with which they are dealing.

Given the shipping papers provided on the next page, answer the questions that follow.

Activity

1. Who is the shipping company of these products?

    _____

2. What is the shipper's number?

    _____

3. What is the emergency contact telephone number?

    _____

4. What materials are being shipped?

    _____

5. What is the UN number of the product being shipped?

    _____

6. Who is the carrier or the rail car initials and number of this shipment?

_____

7. When was this product shipped?

_____

8. Is this product a hazardous material?

_____

2

Learning Activity 2-3
Interpret a Safety Data Sheet (SDS)

Name _____ **Date** _____

References

Hazardous Materials for First Responders, 4th Edition, pp. 148-149

NFPA® 472, 4.2.1(10)

Introduction

A safety data sheet (SDS) is a detailed information bulletin prepared by the manufacturer or importer of a chemical. A SDS describes several items regarding the product, including:

- Hazardous ingredients
- Physical and chemical properties
- Physical and health hazards
- Routes of exposure
- Precautions for safe handling and use
- Emergency and first-aid procedures
- Control measures for the product

SDSs are often the best source of detailed information for a particular material to which first responders have access. First responders can acquire a SDS from the manufacturer of the material, the supplier, the shipper, an emergency response center, or the facility hazard communication plan. SDSs are sometimes attached to shipping papers and containers as well.

Study the SDS provided with this activity, and answer the questions that follow.

Noakes-Miller Inc.

Date Prepared: 04/24/2010
Date Printed: 07/21/2010

BUTYLENE OXIDE-1,2

1. CHEMICAL PRODUCT AND COMPANY IDENTIFICATION

Material Identity
Product Name: BUTYLENE OXIDE-1,2
General or Generic ID: EPOXIDE

Company	Emergency Telephone Number:
Noakes-Miller Inc.	1-555-333-4444
P.O. Box 721	24 hours every day
Anytown, OK 11111	
555-777-8888	

2. HAZARDS IDENTIFICATION

Potential Health Effects

Eye	Contact may cause irritation of the eyes.
Skin	Contact may cause mild skin irritation. Prolonged or repeated exposure may cause blistering of the skin.
Inhalation	Breathing 1,2-Butylene Oxide can irritate the nose, throat, and lungs causing coughing, wheezing, and/or shortness of breath. High exposure may lead to lightheadedness or loss of consciousness.

Target Organ Effects

Developmental Information

Cancer Information	1,2-Butylene Oxide may be a carcinogen in humans
Primary Route(s) of Entry	Inhalation, through the skin, ingestion

3. COMPOSITION/INFORMATION ON INGREDIENTS

Ingredient(s)	CAS Number	% (by weight)
1,2-EPOXYBUTANE	106-88-7	100.0

4. FIRST AID MEASURES

Eyes	If symptoms develop, move victim into fresh air. Flush eyes with water for at least 15 minutes while holding eyelids apart; seek medical attention immediately.
Skin	Remove contaminated clothing. Flush exposed skin with lots of water. If skin is damaged, seek immediate medical attention. If skin is not damaged and symptoms persist, seek medical attention.

Swallowing	Seek medical attention immediately. If individual is drowsy or unconscious, do not give fluids or anything by mouth. Contact a physician, medical facility, or poison control center for advice.
Inhalation	If symptoms develop, immediately move victim into fresh air. Seek immediate medical attention. Keep individual warm and quiet. If individual is not breathing, begin artificial respiration. If heart has stopped, initiate CPR.

5. FIRE FIGHTING MEASURES

Flash Point	-7 F (-22 C)
Explosive Limit	Vol % in air: 3.9 - 20.6
Autoignition Temperature	439 C
Hazardous Products of Combustion	May form: carbon dioxide, carbon monoxide, and other toxic gases.
Fire and Explosion Hazards	This material gives off vapors that are heavier than air. They may travel along the ground or be moved by ventilation. Vapors may be ignited by pilot lights or other distant ignition sources.
Extinguishing Media	Carbon dioxide, dry chemical, water fog. Water may be ineffective.
Fire Fighting Instructions	Wear positive pressure SCBA with appropriate turn-out gear and appropriate chemical resistant personal protective equipment.
NFPA Rating	Health - 2, Flammability - 3, Reactivity - 2

6. ACCIDENTAL RELEASE MEASURES

Spills	Evacuate danger area in case of large spills and contact emergency response agency. Collect leaking liquid in sealable containers. Absorb remaining liquid in sand or inert absorbent and remove to safe place. Do NOT wash away into sewer. Remove / extinguish all ignition sources.

7. HANDLING AND STORAGE

Handling	Source of ignition such as smoking and open flames are prohibited in locations where this material is used, handled, or stored. Metal containers involving transfer of this material should be grounded and bonded. Use only non-sparking tools and equipment when working with 1,2-Butylene Oxide, particularly when opening and closing containers. Even empty containers may contain flammable vapors or residue.

8. EXPOSURE CONTROLS/PERSONAL PROTECTION

Eye Protection	Chemical splash goggles.
Skin Protection	Wear resistant gloves such as: neoprene, To prevent repeated or prolonged skin contact, wear impervious clothing and boots.

Respiratory Protections	Where potential for overexposure exists, use a NIOSH/MSHA approved air supplied respirator. Engineering controls may also be implemented to reduce exposure.
Engineering Controls	Provide sufficient ventilation to maintain exposure below level of overexposure.
Exposure Guidelines	No exposure limits established

9. PHYSICAL AND CHEMICAL PROPERTIES

Boiling Point	63.3 C
Vapor Pressure	207 mmHg at 68 F (20 C)
Specific Vapor Density	2.49 @ AIR=1
Specific Gravity	.826 @ 68.00 F (20 C)
Liquid Density	6.880 lbs/gal @ 68.00 F (20 C) .826 kg/l @ 20.00 C
Description	Colorless liquid with disagreeable odor

10. STABILITY AND REACTIVITY

Hazardous Polymerization	The substance may polymerize on contact with acids, alkalies, tin, aluminium, and iron chlorides, with fire or explosion hazard. Reacts with strong oxidants (such as peroxides) causing fire hazard. Avoid exposure to excessive heat and polymerization catalysts.
Hazardous Decomposition	May form: carbon dioxide and carbon monoxide, various hydrocarbons.
Chemical Stability	Stable.
Incompatibility	Avoid contact with: strong alkalies, strong mineral acids, strong oxidizing agents.

11. TOXICOLOGICAL INFORMATION

No data

12. ECOLOGICAL INFORMATION

No data

13. DISPOSAL CONSIDERATION

Waste Management Information	Contact local, state or federal authorities for specific recommendations.

14. TRANSPORT INFORMATION

DOT Information - 49 CFR 172.101
  DOT Description:
    1,2-BUTYLENE OXIDE, STABILIZED,3,UN 3022,II

Container/Mode:
55 GAL DRUM/TRUCK PACKAGE

NOS Component:
1,2 BUTYLENE OXIDE

RQ (Reportable Quantity) - 49 CFR 172.101
Product Quantity (lbs)   Component
----------------------------------   -------------------------------
           100   1,2-BUTYLENE OXIDE

15. REGULATORY INFORMATION

US Federal Regulations
TSCA (Toxic Substances Control Act) Status
TSCA (UNITED STATES) The intentional ingredients of this product are listed.

CERCLA RQ - 40 CFR 302.4(a)
Component   RQ (lbs)
----------------------------------   ---------
1,2-BUTYLENE OXIDE   100

SARA 302 Components - 40 CFR 355 Appendix A
None

Section 311/312 Hazard Class - 40 CFR 370.2
Immediate(X) Delayed( ) Fire(X) Reactive(X) Sudden Release of Pressure( )

SARA 313 Components - 40 CFR 372.65
Section 313 Component(s)   CAS Number   %
---   -------------------
1,2-BUTYLENE OXIDE   106-88-7 100.00

International Regulations
Inventory Status
Not determined

State and Local Regulations
California Proposition 65
None

16. OTHER INFORMATION

The information provided in this SDS was derived from a variety of sources, none of which warrant complete accuracy of their information. Therefore, while the information provided in this SDS is believed to be correct, Noakes-Miller Inc. cannot guarantee it.

1. What is the chemical name for this product?

_____

2. What is the CAS® number for this product?

_____

3. What are the potential health effects if this product is inhaled?

_____

_____

_____

4. What first aid measures should be taken if this product comes in contact with the eyes?

_____

_____

_____

5. What section of this SDS describes what to do in the event of a spill?

_____

6. What unusual fire and explosion hazards are associated with this material?

_____

_____

_____

_____

_____

_____

7. What respiratory protection should be worn when dealing with this product?

_____

_____

_____

8. What is the NFPA® health rating for this product?

_____

9. Describe the physical properties that could be used to identify this product, including appearance, color, and odor?

_____

_____

_____

10. What is the chemical stability of this product?

_____

Chapter 3

Awareness-Level Actions at Hazardous Materials Incidents

Terms

Write the definition of the terms below on the blanks provided.

1. Incidental Release (167) _____

   _____

2. Toxic Inhalation Hazard (TIH) (172) _____

   _____

3. Initial Isolation Distance (173) _____

   _____

4. Structural Firefighters' Protective Clothing (174) _____

   _____

5. Self-Contained Breathing Apparatus (SCBA) (175) _____

   _____

6. Chemical Protective Clothing (CPC) (175) _____

   _____

7. Street Clothes (174) _____

   _____

8. Evacuation (175) _____

   _____

9. Shelter in Place (175) _____

   _____

10. Cross Contamination (177) _____

_____

11. Decontamination (Decon) (176) _____

_____

12. Protective Action Distance (177) _____

_____

13. Initial Isolation Zone (179) _____

_____

14. Isolation Perimeter (181) _____

_____

True/False

Write True or False on the blanks provided; if False, write the correct statement on the lines provided.

_____ 1. Operational procedures that are standardized, clearly written, and mandated to each department/organization member establish accountability and decrease command and control effectiveness. (170)

_____

_____

_____ 2. For fixed-facility responders, notification may be as simple as dialing 9-1-1 to report an incident. (170)

_____

_____

_____ 3. When consulting chemical reference sources for information about a particular substance, no more than one reference source should be consulted to ensure information is complete and accurate. (172)

_____

_____

_____ 4. The orange-bordered pages of the ERG provide an index of dangerous goods in alphabetical order by material name so that the first responder can quickly identify the Guide to consult for the name of the material involved. (172)

_____

_____

_____ 5. Common recommendations for first aid at hazardous materials incidents include calling for emergency medical service assistance, moving victims to fresh air, and flushing contaminated skin and eyes with running water. (176)

_____

_____

_____ 6. A large spill can involve multiple spills. (177)

_____

_____

_____ 7. The warmer, more active atmosphere normal during the day assembles chemical contaminants more readily than the cooler, calmer conditions common at night. (178)

_____

_____

_____ 8. Contact numbers for emergency response centers are provided in the white pages in both the front and the back of the ERG. (179)

_____

_____

_____ 9. An emergency response center will provide immediate technical assistance to a caller. (179-180)

_____

_____

_____ 10. Awareness-Level personnel can be considered witnesses because they are near or at the scene when an incident or attack occurs. (183)

_____

_____

3

Short Answer

Write the correct answers on the blanks provided.

1. What are the responsibilities of Awareness-Level personnel when faced with an incident involving hazardous materials? (167)

    _____

    _____

    _____

    _____

2. Provide examples of the type of personal protective clothing and equipment that should be worn at haz mat incidents. (174)

    _____

    _____

    _____

    _____

3. List information a responder should collect and provide to an emergency response center. (179-180)

    _____

    _____

    _____

    _____

    _____

    _____

    _____

    _____

    _____

Multiple Choice

Write the correct answers on the blanks provided.

_____ 1. OSHA 29 CFR 1910.120 requires emergency response organizations in the U.S. to develop emergency response plans that must cover all the following EXCEPT: (169)
   A. decontamination.
   B. safe distances and places of refuge.
   C. environmental harm and danger to animals.
   D. personnel roles, lines of authority, training, and communication.

_____ 2. All of the following are ways to locate the appropriate initial action guide page EXCEPT: (171)
   A. use the name of the material in the blue-bordered section of the guidebook.
   B. use the container profiles provided in the yellow pages in the back of the book.
   C. identify the transportation placard of the material and then use the associated placard in Table of Placards.
   D. identify the four-digit U.N. identification number on a placard and then look up the appropriate guide in the yellow-bordered pages of the guidebook.

_____ 3. The highest potential hazard is listed _____ in the potential hazards section. (173)
   A. last
   B. first
   C. in color
   D. separately

_____ 4. Which section of the ERG contains a table that lists (by ID number) TIH materials? (175)
   A. Evacuation
   B. Shelter in place
   C. Isolation perimeter
   D. Initial isolation and protective action distances

_____ 5. In which sections of the ERG are green-highlighted chemicals found? (175)
   A. First aid
   B. Spill or leak
   C. Orange-bordered pages
   D. Yellow-and blue-bordered pages

_____ 6. Which of the following is NOT a potential ignition source? (176)
   A. Camera
   B. Open water
   C. Static electricity
   D. Turning on a flashlight

_____ 7. Which of the following can sometimes be called secondary contamination? (177)

    A. Evacuation

    B. Decontamination

    C. Cross contamination

    D. Primary contamination

_____ 8. Which pages of the ERG provide an index list of hazardous materials in numerical order of ID number? (172)

    A. Blue

    B. White

    C. Yellow

    D. Orange

_____ 9. An outer boundary of an incident that is controlled to prevent entrance by the public or unauthorized persons is called a (an): (181)

    A. hazard zone.

    B. traffic cordon.

    C. incident boundary.

    D. isolation perimeter.

3

Crossword

Across

4 Contamination of people, equipment, or the environment outside the hot zone without contacting the primary source of contamination.

7 Outer boundary of an incident that is controlled to prevent entrance by the public or unauthorized persons.

10 Downwind distance from a hazardous materials incident within which protective actions should be implemented.

11 Controlled process of leaving or being removed from a potentially hazardous location, typically involving relocating people from an area of danger or potential risk to a safer place.

12 Circular zone (with a radius equivalent to the initial isolation distance) within which persons may be exposed to dangerous concentrations upwind of the source and may be exposed to life-threatening concentrations downwind of the source.

Down

1 Clothing designed to shield or isolate individuals from the chemical, physical, and biological hazards that may be encountered during operations involving hazardous materials.

2 Process of removing a hazardous, foreign substance from a person, clothing, or area.

3 Clothing that is anything other than chemical protective clothing or structural firefighters' protective clothing, including work uniforms and ordinary civilian clothing.

5 Liquid or gas known to be a severe hazard to human health during transportation.

6 Distance within which all persons are considered for evacuation in all directions from a hazardous materials incident.

8 Spill or release of a hazardous material where the substance can be absorbed, neutralized, or otherwise controlled at the time of release by employees in the immediate release area.

9 Having occupants remaining in a structure or vehicle in order to provide protection from a rapidly approaching hazard (fire, hazardous gas cloud, etc.). Opposite of evacuation.

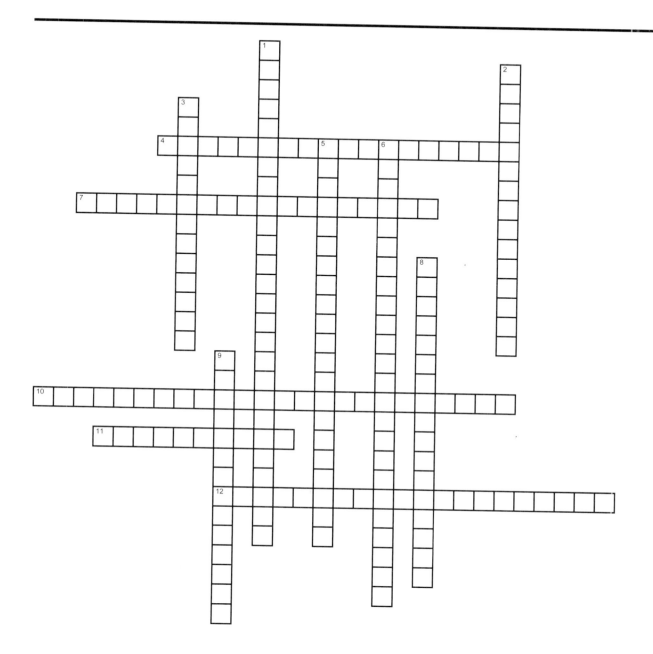

Skill Sheet 3-1

Objective 4: Obtain information about a hazardous material using the *Emergency Response Guidebook (ERG [NFPA® 472, 4.2.3, 4.4.2]*

Student Name: _____ **Date:** _____

Directions

For this skills evaluation checklist, students will obtain information about a hazardous material using the *Emergency Response Guidebook (ERG)*. Students will obtain information in the following ways: using the U.N. identification number, using the material name, container profile, and placard.

Equipment & Materials

- *Emergency Response Guidebook (ERG)*
- Material names
- Placards
- Container profile pictures
- U.N. I.D. numbers

Task Steps

Using the U.N. Identification Number

1. Identify the four-digit U.N. identification number.
2. Refer to the appropriate yellow-bordered pages to find the correct reference guide number.
3. Refer to the orange-bordered page with the appropriate guide number for information on managing the incident.
4. For highlighted chemicals refer to the green-bordered pages for initial isolation by looking up the identification number.

Using the Material Name

1. Identify the name of the material.
2. Refer to the name of the material in the blue-bordered pages to locate the correct guide number.
3. Refer to the orange-bordered page with the appropriate guide number for information on managing the incident.
4. For highlighted chemicals refer to the green-bordered pages for initial isolation by looking up the identification number.

Using the Container Profile

1. Identify the profile of the container and locate the profile in the white pages of the *ERG*.
2. Refer to the appropriate guide number in the circle and go to the appropriate orange-bordered page.

Using the Placard

1. Identify the placard and locate it in the white pages of the *ERG*.
2. Refer to the appropriate guide number in the circle and go to the appropriate orange-bordered page.

Chapter 4

Chemical Properties and Hazardous Materials Behavior

Terms

Write the definition of the terms below on the blanks provided.

1. Autoignition Temperature (194) _____

   _____

2. Flammability (194) _____

   _____

3. Flash Point (194) _____

   _____

4. Fire Point (196) _____

   _____

5. Nonflammable (196) _____

   _____

6. Carbon Monoxide (CO) (197) _____

   _____

7. Hydrogen Cyanide (HCN) (198) _____

   _____

8. Carbon Dioxide (CO_2) (198) _____

   _____

9. Lower Explosive Limit (LEL) (198) _____

   _____

10. Upper Explosive Limit (UEL) (198) _____

_____

11. Vapor Pressure (200) _____

_____

12. Boiling Point (202) _____

_____

13. Boiling Liquid Expanding Vapor Explosion (BLEVE) (202) _____

_____

14. Vapor Density (204) _____

_____

15. Water Solubility (205) _____

_____

16. Polar Solvents (205) _____

_____

17. Miscibility (205) _____

_____

18. Specific Gravity (205) _____

_____

19. Persistence (207) _____

_____

20. Dispersion (207) _____

_____

21. Reactive Material (207) _____

_____

22. Activation Energy (208) _____

_____

23. Strong Oxidizer (209) _____

_____

24. Inhibitor(s) (209) _____

_____

25. General Emergency Behavior Model (GEBMO) (211) _____

_____

26. Engulf (218) _____

_____

27. Hemispheric Release (219) _____

_____

28. Cloud (220) _____

_____

29. Plume (220) _____

_____

30. Cone (221) _____

_____

4

Matching

Write the correct answers on the blanks provided.

_____ 1. Solid particle that is formed or generated from solid organic or inorganic materials by reducing its size through mechanical processes such as crushing, grinding, drilling, abrading, or blasting (194)

_____ 2. Suspension of particles that form when material from a volatilized (vapor state) solid condenses in cool air (194)

_____ 3. Finely divided liquid suspended in the atmosphere (194)

_____ 4. Form of mist characterized by highly respirable, minute liquid particles (194)

_____ 5. Solid particle whose length is several times greater than its diameter (194)

_____ 6. Gaseous form of a substance that is normally in a solid or liquid state at room temperature and pressure (194)

A.   Aerosol

B.   Dust

C.   Fiber

D.   Fume

E.   Mist

F.   Vapor

True/False

Write True or False on the blanks provided; if False, write the correct statement on the lines provided.

_____ 1. A hazardous material's state of matter influences its behavior. (193)

_____

_____

_____ 2. Gases are the easiest state of matter to contain for mitigation purposes. (193)

_____

_____

_____ 3. The term inflammable means the same thing as flammable in many parts of the world. (196)

_____

_____

_____ 4. The greater the flash point, the lower the fire hazard (196)

_____

_____

_____ 5. Vapor pressure can be used as a general gauge to tell how fast a product will evaporate under normal circumstances. (201)

_____

_____

_____ 6. Melting point is the temperature at which a liquid changes to a gas at a given pressure. (202)

_____

_____

_____ 7. The majority of gases have a vapor density greater than 1. (204)

_____

_____

_____ 8. If water and gasoline were combined, they will mix easily. (205)

_____

_____

_____ 9. The stronger the oxidizer, the stronger the reaction. (209)

_____

_____

_____ 10. Materials that may undergo violent polymerization if subjected to heat or contamination are designated with a V in the blue and yellow sections of the ERG. (209)

_____

_____

_____ 11. Some substances will sublime or change directly from a solid into a gas without going into a liquid state in between. (203)

_____

_____

_____ 12. If a rapid release occurs in a ton container, cargo tank, or tank car, the release occurs a longer period of time and may have a greater effect than would a breach in a 150-pound cylinder. (218)

_____

_____

_____ 13. A cloud dispersion is a semicircular or dome-shaped pattern of airborne hazardous materials that is still partially in contact with the ground or water. (219)

_____

_____

_____ 14. Thermal hazards cause harm during hazardous materials incidents. (225)

_____

_____

Short Answer

Write the correct answers on the blanks provided.

1. What does the acronym BLEVE stand for? (202)

_____

_____

2. What are examples of catalysts during chemical reactions? (209)

_____

_____

_____

_____

_____

3. Hazardous materials incidents have what common elements? (211-214)

_____

_____

_____

4. What are the types of exposures to consider in hazard and risk assessment? (224)

_____

_____

_____

Multiple Choice

Write the correct answers on the blanks provided.

_____ 1. The _____ is commonly used to determine how flammable a liquid is. (196)
  A. fire point
  B. flash point
  C. flammability
  D. autoignition temperature

_____ 2. The flash point used to determine whether a liquid is combustible for OSHA is: (196)
  A. 141°F (60.5°C) or less.
  B. less than 140°F (60°C).
  C. 100°F (38°C) or greater.
  D. greater than 141°F (60.5°C).

_____ 3. Which of the following is a byproduct of the incomplete combustion of organic materials? (197)
  A. Oxygen
  B. Carbon dioxide
  C. Carbon monoxide
  D. Hydrogen cyanide

_____ 4. What acts as a simple asphyxiant by displacing oxygen? (198)
  A. Carbon dioxide
  B. Hydrogen fluoride
  C. Carbon monoxide
  D. Hydrogen cyanide

_____ 5. Which of the following statements regarding vapor pressure is LEAST accurate? (200)
  A. It can be expressed in psi, kPa, mmHg, or atm.
  B. It can be viewed as the measure of the tendency of a substance to evaporate.
  C. It is pressure exerted by saturated vapor above its own liquid in a closed container.
  D. It is the temperature of a substance when the vapor pressure equals or exceeds atmospheric pressure.

_____ 6. Examples of materials with a _____ less than 1 include helium, neon, acetylene, and hydrogen. (204)
  A. melting point
  B. vapor density
  C. freezing point
  D. ignition temperature

_____ 7. Materials with a _____ less than 1 will float in (or on) water. (205)

    A. dispersion rate
    B. water solubility
    C. specific gravity
    D. activation energy

_____ 8. The _____ of a chemical is its ability to remain in the environment. (207)

    A. persistence
    B. dispersion rate
    C. specific gravity
    D. activation energy

_____ 9. Substances that react vigorously or violently with the air, water, heat, light, or each other are called: (207)

    A. inhibitors.
    B. polar solvents.
    C. strong oxidizers.
    D. reactive materials.

_____ 10. Time-sensitive _____ are added to liquid styrene when it is shipped in order to prevent the styrene from polymerizing during transport. (209-211)

    A. inhibitors
    B. stabilizers
    C. oxidizers
    D. reactive materials

_____ 11. What is the correct sequence for hazardous material incidents? (214-215)

    A. Stress-Breach-Release-Dispersion-Exposure-Harm
    B. Harm-Stress-Breach- Release-Dispersion-Exposure
    C. Exposure-Harm-Stress-Dispersion-Breach-Release
    D. Dispersion-Breach-Release-Stress-Exposure-Harm

_____ 12. Which of the following is NOT a common stressor? (215-216)

    A. Material
    B. Thermal
    C. Chemical
    D. Mechanical

_____ 13. Which of the following is an example of a breach? (216-217)

    A. Spill
    B. Puncture
    C. Rapid relief
    D. Detonation

_____ 14. An irregularly shaped pattern of airborne hazardous materials where wind and/or topography influence the downrange course from the point of release is called a: (220)

    A. cone.

    B. cloud.

    C. stream.

    D. plume.

4

Across

1 Two or more liquids' capability to mix together.

5 Colorless, toxic gas with a faint odor similar to bitter almonds; produced by the combustion of nitrogen-bearing substances.

10 Incapable of combustion under normal circumstances; normally used when referring to liquids or gases.

12 Triangular-shaped pattern of an airborne hazardous material release with a point source at the breach and a wide base downrange.

14 Maximum concentration of vapor or gas in air that will allow combustion to occur.

17 Material that encourages a strong reaction (by readily accepting electrons) from a reducing agent (fuel).

19 Material that is added to products that easily polymerize in order to control or prevent an undesired reaction.

20 Amount of energy that must be added to an atomic or molecular system to begin a reaction.

22 Colorless, odorless, dangerous gas formed by the incomplete combustion of carbon.

23 Dome-shaped pattern of airborne hazardous material still partially in contact with ground or water.

26 Minimum temperature at which a liquid gives off enough vapors to form an ignitable mixture with air near the surface of the liquid.

27 Measure of the tendency of a substance to evaporate.

Down

2 Temperature of a substance when the vapor pressure equals or exceeds atmospheric pressure.

3 Lowest percentage of fuel/oxygen mixture required to support combustion.

4 Fuel's susceptibility to ignition.

6 Substance capable of or tending to react chemically with other substances.

7 Ability of a liquid or solid to mix with or dissolve in water.

8 Irregularly shaped pattern of an airborne hazardous material where wind influences the downrange course.

9 Act or process of being spread widely.

11 Weight of a given volume of pure vapor or gas compared to the weight of an equal volume of dry air at the same temperature and pressure.

12 Colorless, odorless, heavier than air gas that neither supports combustion nor burns.

13 No external ignition source is required because the material itself has been heated to ignition.

15 Flammable liquids that have an attraction for water.

16 Weight of a substance compared to the weight of an equal volume of water at a given temperature.

18 Length of time a chemical agent remains effective without dispersing.

21 Temperature at which a liquid fuel produces sufficient vapors to support combustion once the fuel is ignited.

24 Dispersion of material as defined in the General Hazardous Materials Behavior Model (GEBMO).

25 Ball-shaped pattern of an airborne hazardous material where the material has collectively risen above the ground or water.

Chapter 5

Incident Management

Write the definition of the terms below on the blanks provided.

1. Incident Management System (235) _____

    _____

2. Incident Action Plan (IAP) (236) _____

    _____

3. National Incident Management System - Incident Command System (236) _____

    _____

4. Incident Commander (IC) (236) _____

    _____

5. Command Post (CP) (237) _____

    _____

6. National Response Framework (NRF) (238) _____

    _____

7. Unified Command (240) _____

    _____

8. Safety Officer (245) _____

    _____

9. Plain Language (255) _____

    _____

5

Write True or False on the blanks provided; if False, write the correct statement on the lines provided.

_____ 1. Use of incident management systems is required by NFPA® 1561. (236)

_____ 2. The supervisor is the individual responsible for the management of all incident operations. (236)

_____ 3. The Incident Commander may delegate responsibilities and assign personnel to subordinate management roles. (238)

_____ 4. The disaster medical assistance teams are specialized response forces designed to provide medical care following a nuclear, biological, and/or chemical incident. (242)

_____ 5. The tactical level entails the overall direction and goals of the incident. (243)

_____ 6. A safety officer is a member of the IMS Command Staff responsible to the Incident Commander for monitoring and assessing hazardous and unsafe conditions and developing measures for assessing personnel safety on an incident. (245)

_____ 7. The staging area is where personnel and equipment awaiting assignment to the incident are held. (249)

8. The safe refuge area manager controls all movement of personnel and equipment between the control zones, and is responsible for isolating the control zones and ensuring proper routes. (254)

_____

9. Plain language is designed to eliminate or limit the use of codes and acronyms during incident response. (255)

_____

10. A computer would be considered an internal communication device. (258)

_____

Short Answer

Write the correct answers on the blanks provided.

1. List the three priorities for haz mat incidents (in order). (233)

2. What are the five major operational positions or functions under NIMS? (243)

3. Describe each step for NIMS incident command transfer. (250-251)

4. Provide five examples of internal communication devices. (258)

_____

_____

_____

_____

_____

Multiple Choice

Write the correct answers on the blanks provided.

_____   1. Which of the following is NOT an advantage of the incident management system? (235-236)

A. Position titles
B. Modular organization
C. Manageable span of control
D. Nonintegrated communication

_____   2. Which of the following coupled with standard operating procedures, provide a predetermined set of procedures? (235)

A. Incident Action Plan (IAP)
B. Incident Management System (IMS)
C. National Response Framework (NRF)
D. Emergency Response Guidebook (ERG)

_____   3. The organizational level having responsibility for a specified functional assignment at an incident is called a: (237)

A. group.
B. branch.
C. division.
D. command.

_____   4. What does the National Response Framework (NRF) do? (238)

A. Evaluates and reports conditions
B. Advises command of the needed task and resources
C. Explains how the U.S. effectively manages all-hazards response
D. Ensures that all requisite functions are completed as part of the IAP

_____ 5. When an incident or potential incident is of such severity, magnitude, and/or complexity that additional resources are needed, states generally request: (240)

    A. local mutual aid.
    B. federal assistance.
    C. only state resources.
    D. state and local resources.

_____ 6. Which of the following is NOT one of the NRF's primary missions in the case of a catastrophic terrorist attack? (241)

    A. Save lives
    B. Contain the event
    C. Preserve national security
    D. Advise on response measures

_____ 7. Which of the following is a duty of the safety officer? (246)

    A. Establish the site security plan
    B. Implement appropriate emergency operations
    C. Establish decontamination plan and operations
    D. Identify hazardous situations at the incident scene

_____ 8. The logistics section is responsible for all the following EXCEPT: (248)

    A. facilities.
    B. equipment.
    C. maintenance.
    D. PPE requirements.

_____ 9. Which section is responsible for the direct management of all incident tactical activities? (248)

    A. Staging
    B. Logistics
    C. Planning
    D. Operations

_____ 10. Which of the following has a common identifier of a green flashing light? (247)

    A. Entry leader
    B. Safety officer
    C. Command post
    D. Incident commander

_____ 11. Which of the following is NOT an agency or organization that mitigates hazardous materials incidents? (252)

    A. EMS
    B. Red Cross
    C. Fire service
    D. Law enforcement

_____ 12. Which of the following is responsible for evaluating and prioritizing victims for treatment, collecting information from the victims, and preventing the spread of contamination by these victims? (255)

    A. Assistant Safety Officer
    B. Decontamination Leader
    C. Safe Refuge Area Manager
    D. Site Access Control Leader

_____ 13. Which of the following is a CORRECT evacuation procedure? (257)

    A. Broadcast the message once.
    B. Broadcast a radio message ordering evacuation.
    C. Use appropriate channels to communicate with both the IC and the telecommunicator.
    D. Sound audible warning devices on the apparatus at the incident for short periods of time.

_____ 14. Under NIMS, all radio communications should be transmitted in: (257)

    A. codes.
    B. acronyms.
    C. abbreviations.
    D. plain language.

5

Across

4 Document that provides guidance on how communities, States, the Federal Government, and private-sector and nongovernmental partners conduct all-hazards emergency response.

5 Fire officer whose primary function is to administrate safety within the entire scope of fire department operations.

7 Written or unwritten plan for the disposition of an incident.

8 Communication that can be understood by the intended audience and meets the purpose of the communicator.

Down

1 The designated physical location of the command and control point where the incident commander and command staff function during an incident and where those in charge of emergency units report to be briefed on their respective assignments.

2 System described in NFPA® 1561, Standard on Fire Department Incident Management System, that defines the roles, responsibilities, and standard operating procedures used to manage emergency operations.

3 In the Incident Management System, a shared command role that allows all agencies with responsibility for the incident, either geographical or functional, to manage the incident by establishing a common set of incident objectives and strategies.

6 Person in charge of the incident management system and responsible for the management of all incident operations during an emergency.

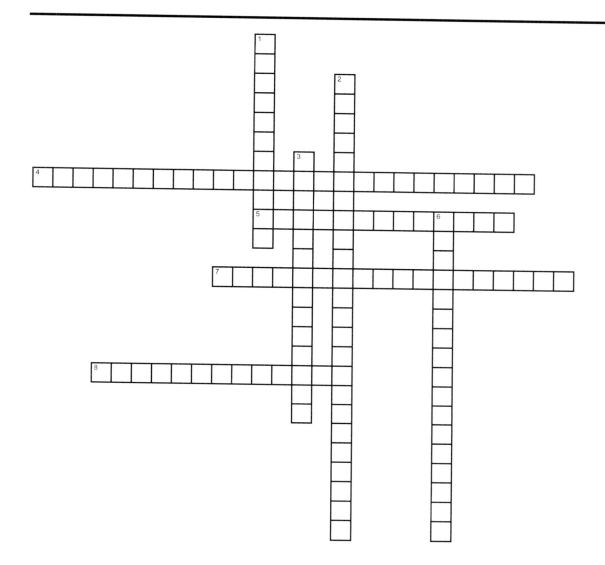

Chapter 6

Strategic Goals and Tactical Objectives

Write the definition of the terms below on the blanks provided.

1. Strategic Goal (265) _____

   _____

2. Tactical Objectives (265) _____

   _____

3. Size-Up (271) _____

   _____

4. Hazard and Risk Assessment (271) _____

   _____

5. Risk (272) _____

   _____

6. Situational Awareness (275) _____

   _____

7. Response Objectives (279) _____

   _____

8. Risk-Based Response (279) _____

   _____

9. Offensive Strategy (280) _____

   _____

10. Defensive Strategy (280) _____

_____

11. Nonintervention Strategy (280) _____

_____

12. Nonintervention Operations (282) _____

_____

13. Defensive Operations (282) _____

_____

14. Offensive Operations (283) _____

_____

15. Hazard-Control Zones (287) _____

_____

16. Hot Zone (288) _____

_____

17. Warm Zone (290) _____

_____

18. Cold Zone (290) _____

_____

19. Staging Area (290) _____

_____

20. Emergency Operations Center (EOC) (293) _____

_____

21. Self-Presenters (301) _____

_____

Fill in the Blank

Put the steps in order by placing the correct step number by each statement.

The Eight Step Incident Management Process: (268)

_____   1. Terminate the incident

_____   2. Information management and resource coordination

_____   3. Hazards and risk evaluation

_____   4. Implement response objectives

_____   5. Identify the problem

_____   6. Site management and control

_____   7. Select personal protective clothing and equipment

_____   8. Decontamination

Matching

Place the correct letter in the blank for each factor. (298)

_____   1. Toxicity

_____   2. Special needs

_____   3. Proximity

_____   4. Wind direction

_____   5. Method of transport

_____   6. Topography

_____   7. Direction of spread

_____   8. Quantity

_____   9. Ability to control and/or stop the release

_____   10. Rate of release

_____   11. Temperature

_____   12. Type of release and dispersion

_____   13. Precipitation

_____   14. Population density

_____   15. Possibility of controlling and/or stopping the release

_____   16. Wind velocity

_____   17. Humidity

A.   Environmental conditions

B.   Material considerations

C.   Population at risk

6

_____ 18. Tides and currents

_____ 19. Warning/notification systems

A. Environmental conditions

B. Material considerations

C. Population at risk

True/False

Write True or False on the blanks provided; if False, write the correct statement on the lines provided.

_____ 1. The A in APIE stands for application. (267)

_____

_____

_____ 2. Skillful ICs are able to quickly identify relevant information and analyze it in order to form a clear picture of the incident. (270)

_____

_____

_____ 3. "How could the material react?" is one of the initial survey questions. (271)

_____

_____

_____ 4. The same as a structure fire, haz mat size-up must consider all six sides of the incident, often referred to as Alpha, Bravo, Charlie, Delta, and the top and bottom. (272)

_____

_____

_____ 5. A Level III incident is a type of incident that requires resources from state/provincial agencies, federal agencies, and/or private industry. (277)

_____

_____

_____ 6. A detail of U.S. NIMS Type 3 incidents is that Operations personnel normally do not exceed 200 per operational period and total incident personnel do not exceed 500. (278-279)

_____

_____

_____ 7. Response objectives are statements based on realistic expectations of what can be accomplished when all allocated resources have been effectively deployed. (279)

_____

_____

_____ 8. Defensive operations are those in which responders seek to confine the emergency to a given area without directly contacting the hazardous materials involved. (282)

_____

_____

_____ 9. An Incident Action Plan (IAP) must never be reevaluated as new information becomes available and circumstances change. (286)

_____

_____

_____ 10. The IC must undertake a health assessment or size-up of the incident in order to determine an appropriate size for the isolation perimeter. (286)

_____

_____

_____ 11. The warm zone is the location where incident personnel and equipment are assigned on an immediately available status. (290)

_____

_____

_____ 12. The federal on-scene coordinator takes command when the party responsible for the chemical release or oil spill is unknown or not cooperative. (293)

_____

_____

_____ 13. A friend system is a system of organizing personnel into workgroups in such a manner that each member has a friend or partner, so that nobody is working alone. (296)

_____

_____

_____ 14. Responders can protect themselves by using time, distance, and shielding. (297)

_____

_____

_____ 15. The US&R designated signal for evacuate the area is one long blast. (297-298)

_____

_____

_____ 16. The decision to shelter in place may be used in a situation when vapors are heavier than air and people are in high-rise structure. (301)

_____

_____

_____ 17. One very important step in the debriefing process is to provide information to personnel concerning the signs and symptoms of overexposure to hazardous materials. (305)

_____

_____

_____ 18. The termination phase involves two procedural actions: critiques and evaluations. (306)

_____

_____

Short Answer

Write the correct answers on the blanks provided.

1. What are the elements of the basic four-step problem-solving formula by George Polya? (266)

_____

_____

_____

_____

2. List the three incident-based elements affecting the selection of strategic mode. (280-281)

_____

_____

_____

3. Provide the elements of an IAP. (284-285)

_____

_____

_____

_____

_____

_____

_____

_____

_____

_____

_____

_____

4. List the factors that must be addressed by the IC in large-scale evacuations. (299-300)

_____

_____

_____

_____

5. What are the major goals of the recovery phase? (305)

_____

_____

_____

6. What information should be obtained during the debriefing stage from responders? (305)

_____

_____

_____

6

Write the correct answers on the blanks provided.

_____ 1. What are prioritized depending on available resources and the particulars of the incident? (266)
   A. Strategic goals
   B. Tactical objectives
   C. Defensive objectives
   D. Offensive operations

_____ 2. GEDAPER was developed by: (267)
   A. David Lesak.
   B. Gregory Noll.
   C. George Polya.
   D. Ludwig Benner.

_____ 3. The D in OODA stands for: (268)
   A. details.
   B. decide.
   C. develop.
   D. distinguish.

_____ 4. The RAIN concept can be used to _____ objectives at Weapon of Mass Destruction (WMD) incidents. (268)
   A. analyze
   B. simplify
   C. develop
   D. complicate

_____ 5. Which of the following is the assessment of incident conditions and recognition of cues indicating problems and potential problems presented by an incident? (271)
   A. Size-up
   B. Offensive strategy
   C. Risk-based response
   D. Hazard and risk assessment

_____ 6. Which of the following is NOT an action an IC can do to process more information relevant to size-up? (273)
   A. Note arrival time of other responding units
   B. Review hydrant and water supply conditions
   C. Interview witnesses at the scene upon arrival
   D. Make preliminary plans for apparatus placement at the scene

_____ 7. An incident that is NOT beyond the capabilities of the first responders on the scene is: (275)

    A. Level I.
    B. Level II.
    C. Level III.
    D. Level IV.

_____ 8. Incidents that activate the federal response plan are: (278)

    A. Level I.
    B. Level II.
    C. Level III.
    B. Level IV.

_____ 9. The U.S. NIMS incident type in which the incident is usually limited to one operational period in the control phase is: (278)

    A. Type 1.
    B. Type 2.
    C. Type 3.
    D. Type 4.

_____ 10. A (An) _____ strategy includes actions to control the incident, such as plugging a leak. (280)

    A. offensive
    B. defensive
    C. fast attack
    D. nonintervention

_____ 11. Which of the following is NOT a circumstance when nonintervention mode would be selected? (282)

    A. Explosions are imminent
    B. The situation is clearly beyond the capabilities of responders
    C. The facility or LERP calls for it based on a pre-incident evaluation of the hazards present at the site
    D. There is a high impact on the local jurisdiction, requiring additional staff for support functions

_____ 12. Operations in which responders seek to confine the emergency to a given area without directly contacting the hazardous materials involved are called: (282)

    A. offensive.
    B. defensive.
    C. intervention.
    D. nonintervention.

_____ 13. When _____ the response, the IC must maintain contact with the officers and crew and constantly reevaluate the situation. (286)

    A. planning
    B. analyzing
    C. estimating
    D. implementing

14. Which of the following provides for the scene control required at haz mat and terrorist incidents to protect responders from interference by unauthorized persons, helping regulate movement of first responders within zones? (287)

A. Hot zone
B. Cold zone
C. Warm zone
D. Hazard-control zone

15. Which of the following is also called the contamination reduction zone? (290)

A. Hot zone
B. Cold zone
C. Warm zone
D. Hazard-control zone

16. All of the following are measures to protect responders EXCEPT: (295)

A. ensuring accountability of all personnel.
B. providing emergency medical care and first aid.
C. tracking and identifying all personnel working at an incident.
D. staying uphill, upstream, and upwind of hazardous materials.

17. The Urban Search and Rescue (US&R) designated signal to resume operations is: (297-298)

A. no blast.
B. one long blast.
C. three short blasts.
D. one long and one short blast.

18. Which of the following is a factor that affects the ability of personnel to perform a rescue? (302)

A. Operational weaknesses
B. Required additional resources
C. Plan updates and/or required changes
D. Tools, equipment, and other devices needed to affect the rescue

19. Which of the following statements about the protection of the environment and property is MOST accurate? (303)

A. Mist and vapors show a visible sign for ignition.
B. Exposure protection is a defensive control tactic.
C. Water used during fire-control will not become contaminated.
D. Consequences of contamination will always be noticed immediately.

Crossword

Across

7 Mental evaluation process by the operational officer in charge of an incident to determine and evaluate all existing influencing factors used to develop objectives, strategy, and tactics for fire suppression.

10 An individual's perception and comprehension of the details of their surrounding environment, and the understanding of how events occurring in the moment may affect the future.

11 Area between the hot zone and the cold zone, usually containing the decontamination corridor and requiring a lesser degree of personnel protection.

12 Operations in which responders seek to confine the emergency to a given area without directly contacting the hazardous materials involved.

14 Overall plan for incident control established by the Incident Commander in which responders take no direct actions on the actual problem.

16 Location where incident personnel and equipment are assigned on an immediately available status.

17 Overall plan for incident control established by the Incident Commander (IC) in which responders take aggressive, direct action on the material, container, or process equipment involved in an incident.

18 System of barriers surrounding designated areas at emergency scenes intended to limit the number of persons exposed to a hazard and to facilitate its mitigation.

19 Operations in which responders take aggressive, direct action on the material, container, or process equipment involved in an incident.

20 Facility that houses communications equipment, plans, contact/notification list, and staff that are used to coordinate the response to an emergency.

Down

1 Specific operations that must be accomplished to achieve strategic goals.

2 Statements based on realistic expectations of what can be accomplished when all allocated resources have been effectively deployed.

3 Operations in which responders take no direct actions on the actual problem.

4 Safe zone outside of the warm zone where equipment and personnel are not expected to become contaminated and special protective clothing is not required.

5 Overall plan for incident control established by the Incident Commander (IC) that involves protection of individuals and exposures as opposed to aggressive, offensive intervention.

6 Formal review of the hazards and risk that may be encountered while performing the functions of a firefighter or emergency responder.

8 Potentially hazardous area immediately surrounding the incident site requiring appropriate protective clothing and equipment and other safety precautions for entry.

9 Broad statements of desired achievements to control an incident; achieved by the completion of tactical objectives.

13 Method using hazard and risk assessment to determine an appropriate mitigation effort based on the circumstances of the incident.

15 Individuals who seek medical assistance and have not been treated or undergone decontamination at the incident scene.

Chapter 7

Terrorist Attacks, Criminal Activities, and Disasters

Terms

Write the definition of the terms below on the blanks provided.

1. Agroterrorism (316) _____

    _____

2. Cyber Terrorism (316) _____

    _____

3. Explosion (319) _____

    _____

4. Shock Front (320) _____

    _____

5. Blast-Pressure Wave (320) _____

    _____

6. Detonation (322) _____

    _____

7. Deflagration (322) _____

    _____

8. High Explosive (322) _____

    _____

9. Low Explosive (322) _____

    _____

10. Detonator (322) _____

_____

11. Primary Explosive (323) _____

_____

12. Secondary Explosive (323) _____

_____

13. Illicit Laboratory (323) _____

_____

14. Vehicle-Borne Improvised Explosives Device (VBIED) (329) _____

_____

15. Person-Borne Improvised Explosives Device (PBIED) (331) _____

_____

16. Bomb Squad (336) _____

_____

17. Chemical Attack (340) _____

_____

18. Nerve Agent (340) _____

_____

19. Volatility (342) _____

_____

20. Antidote (342) _____

_____

21. Autoinjector (342) _____

_____

22. Blister Agent (343) _____

_____

23. Chemical Asphyxiant (344) _____

_____

24. Choking Agent (347) _____

_____

25. Riot Control Agent (349) _____

_____

26. Antibiotic (352) _____

_____

27. Biological Agent (352) _____

_____

28. Vector (360) _____

_____

29. Universal Precautions (361) _____

_____

30. Pandemic (362) _____

_____

31. Radiation-Emitting Device (RED) (363) _____

_____

32. Radiological Dispersal Weapons (RDW) (363) _____

_____

33. Improvised Nuclear Device (IND) (363) _____

_____

34. Suitcase Bomb (364) _____

_____

35. Inverse Square Law (367) _____

_____

36. Illegal Dump (368) _____

_____

37. Evidence (368) _____

_____

True/False

Write True or False on the blanks provided; if False, write the correct statement on the lines provided.

_____   1. Terrorist attacks can occur in any jurisdiction. (312)

_____

_____

_____   2. Anthrax is NOT an example of a weapon of mass destruction. (318)

_____

_____

_____   3. Dynamite is an example of a low explosive. (322)

_____

_____

_____   4. A blasting cap is an example of a initiator. (322)

_____

_____

_____   5. Several oxidizers and fuels can be combined to form improvised explosive materials. (323)

_____

_____

_____ 6. Improvised explosive devices (IEDs)are commercially manufactured. (328)

_____

_____

_____ 7. Pipe bombs are the most common type of IED found in the United States. (329)

_____

_____

_____ 8. A chemical agent attacks the nervous system by affecting the transmission of impulses. (340)

_____

_____

_____ 9. Chlorine's odor is above its permissible exposure limit, so it is already harmful when someone smells it. (348)

_____

_____

_____ 10. Arsine is a blood agent, which also means it is a cyanogen. (344)

_____

_____

_____ 11. Category A of biological agents have the highest priority because they include organisms that pose a risk to national security. (354)

_____

_____

_____ 12. Anthrax is a contagious disease. (360)

_____

_____

_____ 13. Emergency response agencies must include radiation monitoring as a normal part of response to any fire and/or explosion incident. (362)

_____

_____

_____ 14. The first priority at a haz mat crime scene is to preserve evidence. (369)

_____

_____

_____ 15. Natural disasters such as floods, hurricanes, tornadoes, and earthquakes can cause a variety of haz mat issues. (371)

_____

_____

Short Answer

Write the correct answers on the blanks provided.

1. What are the key differences between routine emergencies and a terrorist attack? (314-315)

_____

_____

_____

_____

_____

_____

2. List four indicators that an individual may be a suicide bomber. (335-336)

_____

_____

_____

_____

3. Provide five tactics for radiological incidents. (366-367)

_____

_____

_____

_____

_____

4. What are the problems and hazards associated with illegal dumps? (368)

_____

_____

_____

_____

Multiple Choice

Write the correct answers on the blanks provided.

_____ 1. Any weapon or device that is intended or has the capability to cause death or serious bodily injury to a significant number of people is called a: (316)

     A. nerve agent.
     B. low explosive.
     C. high explosive.
     D. weapon of mass destruction.

_____ 2. The C in CBRNE stands for: (316)

     A. cyber.
     B. caution.
     C. choking.
     D. chemical.

_____ 3. The truck bomb that exploded April 19, 1995, outside the Murrah Federal Building in Oklahoma City was an example of a (an): (319)

     A. triacetonetriperoxide (TATP).
     B. radiation-emitting device (RED).
     C. improvised explosive device (IED).
     D. Person-Borne Improvised Explosives Device (PBIED).

_____ 4. Which of the following is sometimes visible expanding outward from the point of detonation? (320)

     A. Explosion
     B. Shock front
     C. Seismic effect
     D. Triacetonetriperoxide

_____ 5. The suction phase of blast-pressure wave can also be called the _____ phase. (320)

     A. shock
     B. destructive
     C. positive-pressure
     D. negative-pressure

_____ 6. An explosion involving a chemical reaction in which the reaction proceeds at less than the speed of sound is called: (322)

     A. detonation.
     B. deflagration.
     C. primary explosive.
     D. secondary explosive.

_____ 7. Which explosive is designed to detonate only under specific circumstances, and is usually set off by activation energy provided by a primary explosive? (322)

   A. Low
   B. Primary
   C. Propellant
   D. Secondary

_____ 8. Which of the following is constructed of cardboard tubes filled with flash powder and sealed at both ends? (333)

   A. M-device
   B. Pipe bomb
   C. Firework
   D. Plastic bottle bomb

_____ 9. An unusually large battery or an extra battery found under the hood or elsewhere is an indicator of a: (337-338)

   A. improvised nuclear device.
   B. radiation-emitting device.
   C. vehicle-borne improvised explosive.
   D. person-borne improvised explosive.

_____ 10. Which of the following are used for purposes such as mining, demolition, and excavation? (322)

   A. Person-borne devices
   B. Homemade explosives
   C. Improvised explosives
   D. Commercial/Military explosives

_____ 11. Do not use two-way radios or cell phones within a minimum of _____ feet (m) of an explosive device or suspected device. (338)

   A. 200 (61)
   B. 300 (91)
   C. 400 (122)
   D. 500 (152)

_____ 12. Which of the following would it be appropriate to administer an autoinjector? (342)

   A. Hand
   B. Large muscle
   C. Near the heart
   D. Bottom of foot

13. A mustard agent is an example of _____ agent. (344)
    A. blood
    B. nerve
    C. blister
    D. riot control

14. Chemical compounds that irritate the eyes, mouth, throat, lungs, and skin are _____ agents. (349)
    A. blood
    B. nerve
    C. blister
    D. riot control

15. The three hazard categories of toxic industrial materials are high, _____, and low hazard. (352)
    A. fair
    B. neutral
    C. average
    D. medium

16. Which of the following are effective against bacteria? (352)
    A. Rickettsias
    B. Streptomycins
    C. Bacterial agents
    D. Biological toxins

17. First responders should adhere to _____ whenever they have contact with broken or moist skin, blood, or body fluids. (361)
    A. universal protocols
    B. first aid precautions
    C. universal precautions
    D. health department measures

18. Which of the following is described as a very compact and portable nuclear weapon? (364)
    A. Vector
    B. Suitcase bomb
    C. Improvised nuclear device
    D. Radiation-emitting device

7

Across

1 High explosive that is designed to detonate only under specific circumstances.

5 Viruses, bacteria, or their toxins used for the purpose of harming or killing people, animals, or crops.

9 A device used to trigger less sensitive explosives, usually composed of a primary explosive.

11 An animate intermediary in the indirect transmission of an agent that carries the agent from a reservoir to a susceptible host.

14 Small, suitcase-or backpack-sized nuclear weapon.

16 A spring-loaded syringe filled with a single dose of a life-saving drug.

17 Site where chemicals are disposed of illegally.

20 Toxic agent that attacks the nervous system by affecting the transmission of impulses.

22 A terrorist attack directed against agriculture, for example, food supplies or livestock.

25 Explosive material that detonates at a velocity faster than the speed of sound.

27 Shock wave created by rapidly expanding gases in an explosion.

29 Deliberate release of a toxic gas, liquid, or solid that can poison people and the environment.

30 Explosive material that deflagrates, producing a reaction slower than the speed of sound.

31 Supersonic thermal decomposition, which is accompanied by a shock wave in the decomposing material.

32 Substance that reacts to keep the body from being able to use oxygen. Also called blood poison, blood agent, or cyanogen agent.

Down

2 A powerful gamma-emitting radiation source used as a weapon.

3 An epidemic occurring over a very wide area affecting a large proportion of the population.

4 Chemical warfare agent that attacks the lungs causing tissue damage.

6 An illicit nuclear weapon bought, stolen, or otherwise originating from a nuclear state.

7 Chemical compound that temporarily makes people unable to function.

8 A physical or chemical process that results in the rapid release of high pressure gas.

10 The premeditated, politically motivated attack against information, computer systems, computer programs, and data.

12 Physical law in which the amount of radiation present is inversely proportional to the square of the distance.

13 A substance's ability to become a vapor at a relatively low temperature.

15 Chemical warfare agent that burns and blisters the skin.

18 A substance intended for use in warfare or terrorist activities to kill, seriously injure, or incapacitate people.

19 Type of antimicrobial agent made from a mold or a bacterium that kills, or slows the growth of other microbes.

21 Chemical reaction producing vigorous heat and sparks moving through the material at less than the speed of sound.

23 Something legally presented in court that bears on the point in question.

24 Crew of emergency responders trained to deal with explosive devices.

26 Boundary between the pressure disturbance and the ambient atmosphere, water, or earth.

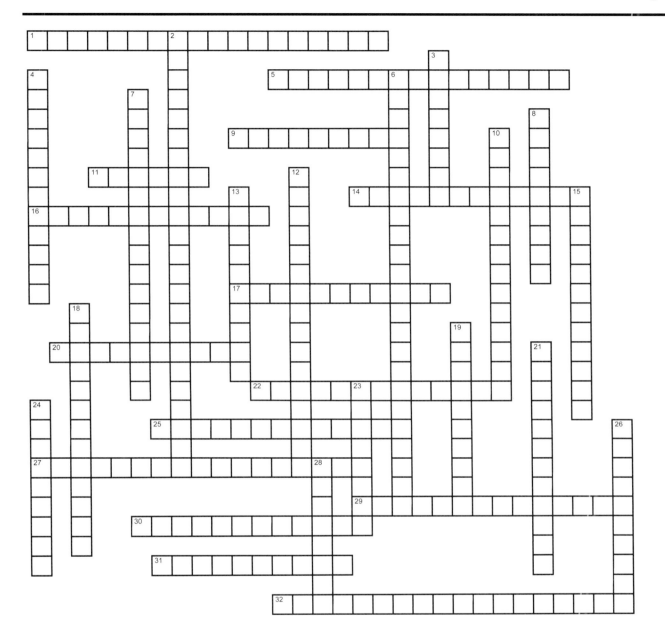

Chapter 8

Personal Protective Equipment

Terms

Write the definition of the terms below on the blanks provided.

1. National Institute for Occupational Safety and Health (NIOSH) (382) _____

    _____

2. Supplied-Air Respirator (SAR) (385) _____

    _____

3. Emergency Breathing Support System (EBSS) (385) _____

    _____

4. Air-Purifying Respirator (APR) (386) _____

    _____

5. Catalyst (387) _____

    _____

6. Sorbent (387) _____

    _____

7. Liquid-Splash Protective Clothing (402) _____

    _____

8. Encapsulating (402) _____

    _____

9. Vapor Protective Clothing (403) _____

    _____

10. Level A Protection (408) _____

_____

11. Level B Protection (408) _____

_____

12. Level C Protection (409) _____

_____

13. Level D Protection (409) _____

_____

14. Joint Service Lightweight Integrated Suit Technology (JSLIST) (418) _____

_____

15. Heat Stroke (420) _____

_____

16. Heat Exhaustion (420) _____

_____

17. Heat Cramps (420) _____

_____

18. Heat Rash (420) _____

_____

19. Frostbite (421) _____

_____

20. Hypothermia (421) _____

_____

21. Trench Foot (421) _____

_____

True/False

Write True or False on the blanks provided; if False, write the correct statement on the lines provided.

_____ 1. The purpose of NIOSH regulation 42 CFR Part 84 is to establish procedures and prescribe requirements that must be met in filing applications for approval by NIOSH of respirators or changes or modifications of approved respirators. (383)

_____

_____

_____ 2. An emergency breathing support system is not certified for firefighting operations because of potential damage to airline from heat, fire, or debris. (385)

_____

_____

_____ 3. Disposable filters, canisters, or cartridges are mounted on one or both sides of a facepiece on an air-purifying respirator. (387)

_____

_____

_____ 4. Dust masks can be used to protect against chemical hazards or small particles such as asbestos fibers. (388)

_____

_____

_____ 5. Current self-contained breathing apparatus (SCBAs) are composed of multiple thermal plastic pressure vessels that are connected. (392)

_____

_____

_____ 6. No single combination or ensemble of protective equipment can protect against all hazards. (392)

_____

_____

8

7. Class 2 ensembles are intended for use at terrorism incidents involving biological or radiological particulate hazards where the concentrations are below immediately dangerous to life and health (IDLH) levels permitting the use of Chemical, Biological, Radiological, and Nuclear (CBRN) compliant air-purifying respirators (APR) or powered air-purifying respirators (PAPR). (395)

_____

_____

8. Structural fire fighting clothing is not a substitute for chemical protective clothing (CPC). (397)

_____

_____

9. A proximity suit is a type of high-temperature clothing that provides greater heat protection than standard structural fire-fighting protective clothing. (400)

_____

_____

10. There are types of CPC that protect against all chemical hazards. (401)

_____

_____

11. Vapor-protective suit materials are tested for permeation resistance against sulfuric acid. (404)

_____

_____

12. Permeation is the process that occurs when a hazardous material enters an opening or a puncture in a protective material. (406)

_____

_____

13. Next generation turnout gear is being designed with greater CBRN protection. (399)

_____

_____

14. Members of SWAT are equipped with the same PPE ensemble as a firefighter. (408)

_____

_____

_____ 15. Overprotection can be hazardous and should be avoided. (413)

_____

_____

_____ 16. A dangerous situation of rapid heat loss may arise for any individual exposed to high winds and cold temperatures. (421)

_____

_____

Matching

Match the correct standard to each statement.

_____ 1. Major requirements include: permissible practices; definitions; respiratory protection program; selection of respirators; medical evaluations; fit testing; use, maintenance, and care of respirators; identification of filters, cartridges, and canisters; training; program evaluation; and record keeping. (383)

_____ 2. Specifies the minimum requirements for the design, performance, testing, and certification of open-circuit self-contained breathing apparatus (SCBA) and combination open-circuit self-contained breathing apparatus and supplied air respirators (SCBA/SAR) for the respiratory protection of fire and emergency responders where unknown, IDLH (immediately dangerous to life and health), or potentially IDLH atmospheres exist. (382-383)

_____ 3. Establishes performance and design requirements to certify SCBA for use in CBRN exposures for use by first responders. (382)

_____ 4. Specifies the minimum requirements for the selection, care, and maintenance of open-circuit self-contained breathing apparatus (SCBA) and combination SCBA/SAR that are used for respiratory protection during fire fighting, rescue, and other hazardous operations. (382)

A. NIOSH Chemical, Biological, Radiological and Nuclear (CBRN) Standard for Open-Circuit Self-Contained Breathing Apparatus (SCBA)

B. NIOSH Standard for Chemical, Biological, Radiological, and Nuclear (CBRN) Full Facepiece Air-Purifying Respirator (APR)

C. NIOSH Standard for Chemical, Biological, Radiological, and Nuclear (CBRN) Air-Purifying Escape Respirator and CBRN Self-Contained Escape Respirator

D. NFPA® 1852, *Standard on Selection, Care, and Maintenance of Open-Circuit Self-Contained Breathing Apparatus (SCBA)*

E. NFPA® 1981, *Standard on Open-Circuit Self-Contained Breathing Apparatus (SCBA) for Emergency Services*

F. OSHA Regulation 29 *CFR* 1910.134, Respiratory Protection

_____ 5. Specifies minimum requirements to determine the effectiveness of escape respirators that address CBRN materials identified as inhalation hazards from possible terrorist events for use by the general working population. (382)

_____ 6. Specifies minimum requirements to determine the effectiveness of full-facepiece APRs (commonly referred to as gas masks) used during entry into CBRN atmospheres that are not immediately dangerous to life and health (IDLH). Atmospheres that are above IDLH concentrations require the use of SCBA. (382)

Matching

Write the correct answers on the blanks provided.

_____ 1. Provides performance and testing requirements for industrial helmets, commonly known as hard hats (396)

_____ 2. Establishes performance criteria and testing requirements for devices used to protect the eyes and face from injuries from impact, non-ionizing radiation and chemical exposure in workplaces and schools (396)

_____ 3. Provides a uniform, authoritative guide for the design, performance specifications, and use of high-visibility and reflective apparel including vests, jackets, bib/jumpsuit coveralls, trousers and harnesses (396)

_____ 4. Provides guidance for selecting the correct gloves that will protect workers and assist employers in compliance with Occupational Safety and Health Administration regulations (396)

_____ 5. Specifies the minimum requirements for the selection, care, use, and maintenance of flash fire protective garments meeting the requirements of NFPA® 2112 (396)

_____ 6. Specifies the minimum design, performance, and certification requirements, and test methods for new flash fire protective garments (396)

A. ANSI/ISEA 105-2005, American National Standard for Hand Protection Selection Criteria

B. ANSI/ISEA 107-2004, American National Standard for High-Visibility Safety Apparel and Headwear

C. ANSI Z87.1-2003, American National Standard for Occupational and Educational Personal Eye and Face Protection Devices

D. ANSI Z89.1-2003, American National Standard for Industrial Head Protection

E. NFPA® 1851, _Standard on Selection, Care, and Maintenance of Protective Ensembles for Structural Fire Fighting and Proximity Fire Fighting_

F. NFPA® 1951, _Standard on Protective Ensembles for Technical Rescue Incidents_

_____ 7. Defines minimum performance criteria, functioning, and test methods for Personal Alert Safety Systems to be used by firefighters engaged in rescue, fire fighting, and other hazardous duties (396)

_____ 8. Specifies requirements for the design, performance, testing, and certification of nonprimary protective station/work uniforms and the individual garments comprising station/work uniforms (396)

_____ 9. Establishes minimum performance requirements for ensembles and ensemble elements to protect first responders from contact with blood- and body-fluid-borne pathogens when providing victim or patient care during emergency medical operations (395)

_____ 10. Specifies minimum design, performance, certification, and documentation requirements; test methods for liquid splash-protective ensembles and liquid splash-protective clothing; and additional optional criteria for chemical flash fire protection (395)

_____ 11. Specifies the minimum selection, care, and maintenance requirements for structural fire fighting protective ensembles (395)

_____ 12. Includes optional protection from CBRN hazards. Only complete ensembles certified as compliant with these additional optional requirements provide this specified level of CBRN protection (395)

_____ 13. Sets performance requirements for protective ensembles used in response to CBRN terrorism incidents; defines three classes of ensembles (Class 2, 3, and 4) based on the protection required for different hazard types (vapors, liquids, and particulates) and airborne contaminant levels (395)

_____ 14. Contains performance requirements for a CBRN Technical Rescue Protective Ensemble for use during entry into CBRN atmospheres not Immediately Dangerous to Life of Health (IDLH); defines limited protection requirements for operational settings where exposure to physical, thermal, liquid, and body fluid-borne pathogen hazards and CBRN agents in vapor, liquid-splash, and particulate forms could be encountered (395)

G. NFPA® 1971, _Standard on Protective Ensembles for Structural Fire Fighting and Proximity Fire Fighting_

H. NFPA® 1975, _Standard on Station/Work Uniforms for Fire and Emergency Services_

I. NFPA® 1982, _Standard on Personal Alert Safety Systems (PASS)_

J. NFPA® 1991, _Standard on Vapor-Protective Ensembles for Hazardous Materials Emergencies_

K. NFPA® 1992, _Standard on Liquid Splash-Protective Ensembles and Clothing for Hazardous Materials Emergencies_

L. NFPA® 1994, _Standard on Protective Ensembles for First Responders to CBRN Terrorism Incidents_

M. NFPA® 1999, _Standard on Protective Clothing for Emergency Medical Operations_

N. NFPA® 2112, _Standard on Flame-Resistant Garments for Protection of Industrial Personnel Against Flash Fire_

O. NFPA® 2113, _Standard on Selection, Care, Use, and Maintenance of Flame-Resistant Garments for Protection of Industrial Personnel Against Flash Fire_

_____ 15. Establishes a minimum level of protection for emergency response personnel against adverse vapor, liquid-splash, and particulate environments during hazardous materials incidents and from specific chemical and biological terrorism agents in vapor, liquid-splash, and particulate environments during CBRN terrorism incidents; ensemble totally encapsulates the wearer and self-contained breathing apparatus (SCBA); addresses Class 1 ensembles (394)

Short Answer

Write the correct answers on the blanks provided.

1. What are the basic types of protective breathing equipment used by responders at haz mat/weapons of mass destruction incidents? (381)

_____

_____

_____

_____

2. List the U.S. OSHA operations that may require the use of CPC. (404-405)

_____

_____

_____

_____

_____

3. On what should the care, cleaning, and maintenance schedules of respiratory protection equipment be based? (423)

_____

_____

_____

Multiple Choice

Write the correct answers on the blanks provided.

_____ 1. Which of the following is a disadvantage of using SCBA-type respirator protection? (384)

    A. Inadequate oxygen levels

    B. Limited air-supply duration

    C. Limited hearing capabilities

    D. Limited lifespan of equipment

_____ 2. Which of the following only protects against specific contaminants at or below certain concentrations? (387)

    A. Supplied-air respirator (SAR)

    B. Air-purifying respirator (APR)

    C. Self contained breathing apparatus (SCBA)

    D. Emergency breathing support system (EBSS)

_____ 3. Which of the following is a precaution that should be taken before using APRs? (388)

    A. Know the limited life of its filters and canisters

    B. Know what chemicals/air contaminants are in the air

    C. Know the carbon dioxide content of the atmosphere before use

    D. Know the temperature for constant monitoring of the atmosphere

_____ 4. Which of the following provides loose fitting, lightweight respiratory protection that can be worn with glasses, facial hair, and beards? (390)

    A. Escape respirator

    B. Supplied-air hood

    C. Combined respirator

    D. Powered air-purifying respirator

_____ 5. Which of the following is NOT a limitation of air supply equipment? (392)

    A. Decreased weight

    B. Limited visibility

    C. Inadequate oxygen levels

    D. Decreased ability to communicate

_____ 6. Which federal regulation applies to five distinct groups of employers and their employees? (396)

    A. OSHA Regulation 29 CFR 1910.156, Fire Brigades

    B. EPA Regulation 40 CFR Part 311, Worker Protection

    C. OSHA Regulation 29 CFR 1910.132, Personal Protective Equipment

    D. OSHA Regulation 29 CFR 1910.120, Hazardous Waste Operations and Emergency Response Standard

7. Structural fire fighting protective clothing may be appropriate for use at haz mat/WMD incidents involving chemical weapons when which of the following conditions are met? (398-399)
   A. Contact with splashes of extremely hazardous materials is likely
   B. The CBRN hazards have been identified and they will rapidly damage or permeate structural fire fighting protective clothing
   C. Total atmospheric concentrations contain high levels of chemicals that are toxic to the skin, and there are no adverse effects from chemical exposure to small areas of unprotected skin
   D. When structural fire fighting protective clothing is the only PPE available; chemical protective clothing is not immediately available; and the incident commander decides it is appropriate after conducting a risk assessment

8. Which of the following is a single, one-piece garment that protects against splashes? (402)
   A. Encapsulating suit
   B. Nonencapsulating suit
   C. Level D protection clothing
   D. Firefighter protective clothing

9. Which of the following provides full body protection against fragmentation, overpressure, impact, and heat? (407)
   A. Body armor
   B. Reusable clothing
   C. Disposable clothing
   D. Bomb disposal suits

10. In the U.S., body armor has been divided by the National Institute of Justice into _____ different categories based on the level of protection provided. (407)
    A. 4
    B. 5
    C. 6
    D. 7

11. The ensemble that provides the highest level of protection for skin, respiratory, and eye protection is _____ protection. (409)
    A. Level A
    B. Level B
    C. Level C
    D. Level D

12. What protection provides liquid-splash protection, but little or no protection against chemical vapors or gases? (410)
    A. Level A
    B. Level B
    C. Level C
    D. Level D

_____ 13. What protection is composed of a splash-protecting garment and an air-purifying device? (411)
   A. Level A
   B. Level B
   C. Level C
   D. Level D

_____ 14. Mission-orientated protective postures provide six flexible levels of protection based on threat level, work rate for the mission, temperature, and: (418)
   A. wind.
   B. humidity.
   C. participants.
   D. precipitation.

_____ 15. Heat _____ is (are) a heat illness resulting from prolonged exposure to high temperatures. (420)
   A. rash
   B. stroke
   C. cramps
   D. exhaustion

_____ 16. The symptoms of heat _____ include weakness, cold and clammy skin, heavy perspiration, rapid and shallow breathing, weak pulse, dizziness, and sometimes unconsciousness. (420)
   A. rash
   B. stroke
   C. cramps
   D. exhaustion

_____ 17. The symptoms for _____ include a tingling and itching sensation, pain, swelling, numbness, cold and blotchy skin. (421)
   A. frostbite
   B. heat rash
   C. trench foot
   D. hypothermia

_____ 18. Which of the following is checked during a medical monitoring evaluation? (422)
   A. Skin
   B. Ulcers
   C. Broken bones
   D. Body mass index

8

Across

5 Respirator with an air-purifying filter, cartridge, or canister that removes specific air contaminates by passing ambient air through the air-purifying element.

8 A substance that influences the rate of chemical reaction between or among other substances.

9 Heat illness resulting from prolonged exposure to high temperatures; characterized by excessive sweating, muscle cramps in the abdomen and legs, faintness, dizziness, and exhaustion.

11 Condition that develops from continuous exposure to heat and humid air; aggravated by clothing that rubs the skin; reduces the individual's tolerance to heat.

12 Foot condition resulting from prolonged exposure to damp conditions or immersion in water.

15 Personal protective equipment that affords the lowest level of respiratory and skin protection.

16 Personal protective equipment that affords a lesser level of respiratory and skin protection than levels A or B.

17 Completely enclosed or surrounded as in a capsule.

18 Abnormally low or decreased body temperature.

Down

1 Chemical protective clothing designed to protect against liquid splashes per the requirements of NFPA® 1992.

2 Gas-tight chemical protective clothing designed to meet NFPA® 1991.

3 Personal protective equipment that affords the highest level of respiratory protection, but a lesser level of skin protection.

4 A material, compound, or system that holds contaminants by adsorption or absorption.

6 An atmosphere-supplying respirator for which the source of breathing air is not designed to be carried by the user; not certified for fire fighting operations.

7 Highest level of skin, respiratory, and eye protection that can be afforded by personal protective equipment (PPE) as specified by the U.S. Environmental Protection Agency (EPA).

10 Local freezing and tissue damage due to prolonged exposure to extreme cold.

13 Heat illness caused by heat exposure, resulting in failure of the body's heat regulating mechanism.

14 Heat illness caused by exposure to excessive heat; symptoms include weakness, cold and clammy skin, heavy perspiration, rapid and shallow breathing, weak pulse, dizziness, and sometimes unconsciousness.

8

Learning Activity 8-1
Given Hazardous Materials Scenarios, Determine Proper PPE for Each Incident and Report and Document the Decision

Name _____ **Date** _____

References

Hazardous Materials for First Responders, 4th Edition, pp. 376-429

NFPA® 472, 6.2.3.1, 6.2.5.1

Introduction

Protective clothing must be worn whenever a wearer faces potential hazards arising from chemical exposure. Typical protective clothing used at haz mat incidents is designed to protect the wearer from heat and hazardous materials contacting the skin or eyes. First responders – particularly those at the Operations Level – must be concerned with safety when choosing and using protecting clothing.

Read the scenarios given below and answer the questions that follow. Use all available hazardous materials references, including the Emergency Response Guidebook.

Scenario 1

An engine company is dispatched to the scene of a motor vehicle accident located on a rural highway. Upon arrival, the engine company officer makes the following observations:

A truck has run off the road and into a ditch. A number of DOT cylinders have come loose and have been thrown from the back of the truck. The cylinders look like the one pictured below and the truck is not placarded. Some of the cylinders are on the roadway, and some have come to rest in the ditch. Several are leaking a green/yellow gas profusely. The driver hands you shipping papers, letting you know that he is transporting chlorine.

1.   What *ERG* guide number is this material?

_____

2. List this material's potential health hazards.

_____

_____

_____

_____

3. What kind of protective clothing should be selected by responders conducting mitigation operations?

_____

_____

_____

_____

Scenario 2

An engine company is dispatched as part of an alarm assignment to a reported dwelling fire. Upon arrival, the officer discovers that the house is not itself on fire, but the rear of a propane delivery truck parked next to the house is. A storage tank, located 100 feet (30 m) to the rear of the dwelling has a hose attached to the fill valve connection on the tank. The house has burned apart approximately 10 feet (3 m) from the rear of the truck with flames coming from the open end. The control valve area of the truck is also involved in fire from the other end of the burned hose. The bottom of the large cylinder on the truck is being impinged by flame. The truck bares the placard below and the number 1978.

4. What is the material that is leaking?

_____

5. What *ERG* Guide Number is this material?

_____

6. List this material's potential fire or explosion hazards.

_____

_____

_____

_____

_____

_____

7. What kind of protective clothing should be selected by responders conducting mitigation operations?

_____

_____

Scenario 3

A local chemical manufacturing plant has notified your response agency that they have a chemical spill at their location. The infirmary is receiving patients who are complaining of breathing difficulty, headache, and sweating. One victim is in a coma. Upon arrival you are directed by plant security to a large storage tank, in the middle of the compound, that appears to have been struck by a vehicle. The tank is leaking and bares the number 2821 and has several placards as shown below.

8. What is the material that is leaking?

_____

9. What _ERG_ Guide Number is this material?

_____

10. What kind of protective clothing should be selected by responders conducting mitigation operations with this material?

_____

_____

_____

_____

_____

_____

Skill Sheet 8-1

Objective 3: Don and doff different types of personal protective equipment (PPE). *[NFPA® 472, 6.2.4.1(3)]*

Student Name: _____ **Date:** _____

Directions

For this skills evaluation checklist, students will don and doff various types of PPE and SCBA.

Equipment & Materials

- *At least two responders*
- *Proper PPE for operation, including Levels A-D equipment*

Task Steps

Level A Suit

1. Perform a visual inspection of PPE and SCBA for damage or defects.
2. Don SCBA. Ensure that the cylinder valve is fully open and that all straps are secured.
3. Don SCBA facepiece and ensure a proper fit and seal.
4. Don Level A suit, placing legs into suit and pulling suit up to waist. Secure inner belt.
5. Don outer boots.
6. Don inner gloves.
7. Place arms in suit and hands into outer gloves.
8. Attach SCBA regulator to facepiece and make sure SCBA is functioning properly.
9. Pull protective hood over head.

   Note: If your AHJ requires a hard hat, don before pulling hood over head.

10. Zip suit enclosure and secure zipper flap.
11. Perform work assignment.
12. After assignment has been performed, proceed to decontamination line.
13. Undergo technical decontamination per AHJ's SOPs.
14. Doff suit and SCBA according to AHJ SOPs, avoiding contact with outer suit or surfaces that may be contaminated.

Level B Suit

1. Perform a visual inspection of PPE for damage or defects.
2. Don non-encapsulating Level B PPE and secure closures.

3. Don work boots.

4. Pull suit leg opening over the top of the work boots.

5. Don SCBA. Ensure that the cylinder valve is fully open and that all straps are secured.

6. Don SCBA facepiece and ensure a proper fit and seal.

7. Pull suit hood up completely so that facepiece straps and skin are not exposed.

   Note: If your AHJ requires a hard hat, don after pulling hood over head.

8. Don inner protective gloves.

9. Don outer protective gloves.

10. Pull suit sleeves over the outside of the gloves.

11. Attach SCBA regulator to facepiece and make sure SCBA is functioning properly.

12. Perform work assignment.

13. After assignment has been performed, proceed to decontamination line.

14. Undergo technical decontamination per AHJ's SOPs.

15. Doff suit and SCBA according to AHJ SOPs, avoiding contact with outer suit or surfaces that may be contaminated.

Level C Suit

1. Perform a visual inspection of PPE for damage or defects.

2. Don non-encapsulating Level C PPE and secure closures.

3. Don work boots.

4. Pull suit leg opening over the top of the work boots.

5. Ensure that the canister is compatible to the hazardous material being encountered.

6. Attach canister to facepiece.

7. Don facepiece and ensure a proper fit and seal.

8. Pull suit hood up completely so that facepiece straps and skin are not exposed.

9. Don inner protective gloves.

10. Don outer protective gloves.

11. Pull suit sleeves over the outside of the gloves.

12. Breathe through APR and ensure that APR is functioning properly.

13. Perform work assignment.

14. After assignment has been performed, proceed to decontamination line.

15. Undergo technical decontamination per AHJ's SOPs.

16. Doff suit and SCBA according to AHJ SOPs, avoiding contact with outer suit or surfaces that may be contaminated.

Structural Fire-Fighting PPE

1. Perform a visual inspection of PPE for damage or defects.

2. Don protective trousers and boots.

3. Don protective hood, pulling hood down around neck and exposing head.

4. Don protective coat.

5. Don SCBA. Ensure that the cylinder valve is fully open and that all straps are secured.

6. Don SCBA facepiece and ensure a proper fit and seal.

7. Attach SCBA regulator to facepiece and make sure SCBA is functioning properly.

8. Pull hood up completely so that facepiece straps and skin are not exposed.

9. Don helmet and secure.

10. Don gloves.

11. Ensure that all fasteners, straps, buckles, etc. are fastened.

12. Ensure that no skin is exposed.

13. Perform work assignment.

14. After assignment has been performed, proceed to decontamination line.

15. Undergo technical decontamination per AHJ's SOPs.

16. Doff PPE and SCBA according to AHJ SOPs, avoiding contact with outer suit or surfaces that may be contaminated.

Chapter 9

Decontamination

Terms

Write the definition of the terms below on the blanks provided.

1. Emergency Decon (435) _____

    _____

2. Mass Decon (435) _____

    _____

3. Technical Decon (435) _____

    _____

4. Triage (440) _____

    _____

5. Allied Professional (445) _____

    _____

True/False

Write True or False on the blanks provided; if False, write the correct statement on the lines provided.

_____   1. Wet methods of decontamination include scraping, brushing, and absorption. (436)

    _____

    _____

_____   2. Chemical methods are used to make the contaminants less harmful by changing them through some kind of chemical process. (437)

    _____

    _____

_____ 3. Nonambulatory patients are victims or responders who are unconscious, unresponsive, or unable to move unassisted. (442)

_____

_____

_____ 4. Deceased victims that do NOT need decontamination at the scene of an event should be touched. (443)

_____

_____

_____ 5. Procedures for conducting triage of patients should be predetermined within the local emergency response plan. (440)

_____

_____

_____ 6. Technical decon may use absorption and adsorption. (446-447)

_____

_____

_____ 7. Removing clothing before showering always decreases potential risk of exposure. (453)

_____

_____

_____ 8. Weapons, ammunition, and other equipment do not need special consideration through the decon process. (461-462)

_____

_____

_____ 9. If temperatures are 64°F (18°C) or lower, consideration should be given to protecting victims from the cold. (463)

_____

_____

_____ 10. Exposure records are not required for all first responders who have been exposed to hazardous materials. (464)

_____

_____

Short Answer

Write the correct answers on the blanks provided.

1. What are the basic principles of any decontamination operation? (435)

_____

_____

_____

2. List five general guidelines for decon operations. (437-440)

_____

_____

_____

_____

_____

3. What are the contributing factors in choosing a decontamination site? (458-459)

_____

_____

_____

_____

_____

_____

_____

Multiple Choice

Write the correct answers on the blanks provided.

_____ 1. During which of the following should life safety primarily take precedence over environmental considerations? (436)

   A. Mass decon with temperature of 0°F.
   B. Technical decon of a granular fertilizer.
   C. Emergency decon of mild acid of work boots.
   D. Triage of non-contaminated victims on a warm spring day.

_____ 2. Which of the following decontamination methods should be used during contaminated clothing removal? (436)

    A. Dry

    B. Wet

    C. Physical

    D. Chemical

_____ 3. Which of the following is NOT a factor that may influence the priority of ambulatory patients? (441)

    A. Victims with conventional injuries

    B. Victims farthest from the point of release

    C. Victims reporting exposure to the hazardous material

    D. Victims with evidence of contamination on their clothing or skin

_____ 4. Which of the following is an instance in which emergency decontamination is needed? (444)

    A. The use of protective clothing

    B. The only victims are nonambulatory

    C. No immediate medical attention is required

    D. Heat illness or other injury suffered by emergency workers in the hot zone

_____ 5. Which of the following is an advantage of emergency decontamination? (445)

    A. Does not require any equipment

    B. Reduces contamination quickly

    C. Totally decontaminates the victim

    D. Does not create contaminated runoff

_____ 6. During technical decon operations, Operations-Level responders will: (445-446)

    A. not wear PPE.

    B. perform physical decontamination activities.

    C. not need to perform other duties and training.

    D. avoid assisting individuals through the decon process.

_____ 7. Which of the following is the physical process of rapidly reducing or removing contaminants from multiple persons in potentially life-threatening situations? (451)

    A. Triage

    B. Mass decon

    C. Technical decon

    D. Emergency decon

_____ 8. Which of the following is NOT an advantage of mass decon? (457)

    A. Reduces contamination quickly

    B. Totally decontaminates the victim

    C. Accommodates large numbers of people

    D. Can be implemented quickly using limited amount of personnel and equipment

_____ 9. Which of the following statements about evaluating effectiveness of decon operations is MOST accurate? (457-458)

    A. Operations cannot be done visually to evaluate effectiveness.
    B. Large groups should be spot checked to determine effectiveness.
    C. An apparatus does not need to undergo decon if it has been exposed.
    D. The same detection equipment cannot be used on both victims and tools.

_____ 10. Which of the following would identify a decontamination corridor? (461)

    A. Safety cones
    B. Fire apparatus
    C. EMS equipment
    D. Red Cross signage

_____ 11. Collection, preservation, and sampling of evidence will be done under the direction of: (464)

    A. fire service.
    B. EMS personnel.
    C. law enforcement.
    D. WMD specialists.

Crossword

Across

4 Individual with the training and expertise to provide competent assistance and direction at haz mat and WMD incidents.

5 A planned and systematic process of reducing contamination to a level that is As Low As Reasonably Achievable (ALARA).

Down

1 The physical process of immediately reducing contamination of individuals in potentially life-threatening situations with or without the formal establishment of a decontamination corridor.

2 Process of decontaminating large numbers of people in the fastest possible time to reduce surface contamination to a safe level.

3 System used for sorting and classifying accident casualties to determine the priority for medical treatment and transportation.

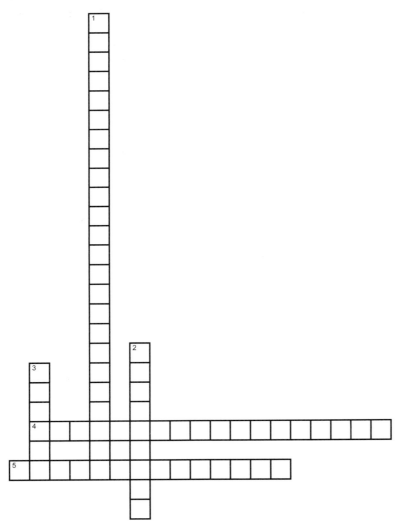

Skill Sheet 9-1

Objective 6: Perform emergency decontamination. *[NFPA® 472, 5.4.1(4)]*

Student Name: _____ **Date:** _____

Directions

For this skills evaluation checklist, students will perform emergency decontamination.

Equipment & Materials

- *Two first responders in full protective clothing*
- *A victim wearing personal protective clothing*
- *A charged hoseline*
- *A scrub brush*

Task Steps

1. Ensure that all responders involved in decontamination operations are wearing appropriate PPE for performing emergency decontamination operations.

2. Remove the victim from the contaminated area.

3. Wash immediately any contaminated clothing or exposed body parts with flooding quantities of water.

4. Remove victims clothing and/or PPE rapidly – if necessary, cutting from the top down in a manner that minimizes the spread of contaminants.

5. Perform a quick cycle of head-to-toe rinse, wash, and rinse.

6. Transfer the victim to treatment personnel for assessment, first aid, and medical treatment.

7. Ensure that ambulance and hospital personnel are told about the contaminant involved.

8. Decontaminate tools.

9. Proceed to decontamination line for decontamination.

Skill Sheet 9-2

Objective 8: Set up and implement a technical decontamination corridor and undergo decontamination.
[NFPA® 472, 6.2.4.1(4), 6.4.4.2(1-2), 6.9.4.1.1(2)]

Student Name: _____ **Date:** _____

Directions

For this skills evaluation checklist, students will perform set up a technical decontamination corridor and undergo decontamination.

Equipment & Materials

- *Tarps, salvage covers, or plastic sheeting*
- *Traffic cones, other means of marking corridor entrance*
- *Catch bins or wading pools*
- *Buckets, drums, or plastic containers for each drop station*
- *Brushes*
- *Large, heavy-duty trash bags*
- *Portable sprayers*
- *Pumps*
- *Scrubbing utensils*
- *Soap*
- *Hoses/water supply, hoseline attachments*
- *Appropriate monitoring/detection devices*
- *Tents*
- *Portable showers*
- *Bags and tags for personal property or evidence*

Task Steps

Set Up a Technical Decontamination Corridor

1. Ensure that all responders are wearing appropriate PPE for establishing the decon corridor and performing technical decontamination operations.
2. Set up the decontamination corridor uphill and upwind from the hot zone, away from remote drains or waterways.
3. Mark entry and exit of decontamination corridor so that they are clearly identified.
4. Set up ground cover (tarp or salvage cover) for secondary contamination and runoff containment.

5. Establish a tool-drop station in the hot zone at the entry to the decontamination corridor.

   Note: The number of stations in the decon corridor will vary depending on the needs of the incident and local SOPs. Law enforcement personnel may need a separate decontamination station for tactical equipment.

6. Establish a gross decontamination station after the tool-drop station in the decontamination corridor.

7. Establish a secondary decontamination station including appropriate cleaning solution(s) as set forth by the haz mat technician, SOPs, or allied professional.

8. Establish a PPE removal station with waste disposal containers for contaminated PPE.

9. Establish a respiratory protection removal station.

   Note: Steps 8 and 9 may need to be reversed, depending on the PPE worn.

10. Establish an undergarment removal station with waste disposal containers for contaminated clothing.

11. Establish shower and clothing change station.

12. Establish a medical evaluation area.

13. Perform technical decontamination operations for persons according to assigned tasks and the AHJ's SOPs.

Undergo Technical Decontamination, Ambulatory Responder

1. Proceed to the first station in the decontamination corridor.

2. Drop tools in collection container.

3. Undergo gross decontamination.

4. Undergo secondary decontamination wash.

5. Remove outer PPE. Place PPE in waste container.

6. Remove respiratory protection, removing facepiece last.

   Note: Steps 5 and 6 may need to be reversed, depending on the PPE worn.

7. Remove undergarments.

8. Shower and wash thoroughly from the top down.

9. Monitor for additional contamination using the appropriate detection device.

   Note: If contamination is detected, repeat decontamination wash and/or change decontamination method, as appropriate.

10. Proceed to medical evaluation station.

Skill Sheet 9-3

Objective 9: Perform technical decontamination on a non-ambulatory victim. *[NFPA® 472, 5.4.4.2(2)]*

Student Name: _____ **Date:** _____

Directions

For this skills evaluation checklist, students will perform technical decontamination on a non-ambulatory victim.

Equipment & Materials

- *Tarps, salvage covers, or plastic sheeting*
- *Traffic cones, other means of marking corridor entrance*
- *Catch bins or wading pools*
- *Buckets, drums, or plastic containers for each drop station*
- *Brushes*
- *Large, heavy-duty trash bags*
- *Portable sprayers*
- *Pumps*
- *Scrubbing utensils*
- *Soap*
- *Hoses/water supply, hoseline attachments*
- *Appropriate monitoring/detection devices*
- *Tents*
- *Portable showers*
- *Bags and tags for personal property or evidence*
- *Carts or skids*
- *Backboard/Stokes® basket*

Task Steps

1. Ensure that all responders are wearing appropriate PPE for performing technical decontamination operations.
2. Establish technical decontamination corridor for non-ambulatory decontamination according to the AHJ's SOPs.
3. Establish an initial triage point to evaluate and direct persons.
4. Perform lifesaving intervention.

5. Transfer the victim to the non-ambulatory wash area of the decontamination station on an appropriate backboard/litter device.

6. Remove all clothing, jewelry, and personal belongings, and place in appropriate containers. Decontaminate as required, and safe-guard. Use plastic bags with labels for identification.

7. Carefully undress non-ambulatory persons, and avoid spreading the contamination when undressing. Do not touch the outside of the clothing to the skin. If biological agents are suspected, a fine water mist can be applied to trap the agent in the clothing and prevent the spread of contamination.

8. Completely wash the victim's entire body using handheld hoses, sponges, and/or brushes and then-rinse.

9. Clean the victim's genital area, armpits, folds in the skin, and nails with special attention. If conscious, instruct the victim to close his/her mouth and eyes during wash and rinse procedures.

10. Transfer the victim from the wash and rinse stations to a drying station after completing the decontamination process. Ensure that the victim is completely dry.

11. Monitor for additional contamination using the appropriate detection device.

    Note: If contamination is detected, repeat decontamination wash and/or change decontamination method, as appropriate.

12. Have on-scene medical personnel reevaluate the victim's injuries.

Skill Sheet 9-4

Objective 11: Perform mass decontamination. *[NFPA® 472, 6.3.4.2]*

Student Name: _____ **Date:** _____

Directions

For this skills evaluation checklist, students will perform mass decontamination.

Equipment & Materials

- *Firefighter outfitted in proper PPE*
- *Fire apparatus*
- *A charged hoseline with fog pattern nozzle*
- *A scrub brush*
- *A secure container with lid*

Task Steps

1. Ensure that all responders are wearing appropriate PPE for performing mass decontamination operations.

2. Prepare fire apparatus for use during mass decontamination.

3. Set fire nozzle to fog pattern.

4. Instruct all victims to go through mass decontamination.

    Note: Non-ambulatory victims should be carried or moved through the decontamination process according to AHJ SOPs. Refer to Skill Sheet 9-3 for specific instructions on performing decontamination of non-ambulatory victims.

5. Instruct victims to remove contaminated clothing, ensuring that victims to not come into further contact with any contaminants.

6. Instruct victims to keep arms raised as they proceed slowly through the wash area.

7. Monitor for additional contamination using the appropriate detection device.

    Note: If contamination is detected, repeat decontamination wash and/or change decontamination method, as appropriate.

8. Instruct victims to move to a clean area to dry off.

9. Send victims for medical treatment.

10. Inform EMS personnel of contaminant involved and its hazards, if known.

11. Document activity log.

Chapter 10

Product Control

Terms

Write the definition of the terms below on the blanks provided.

1. Confinement (477) _____

   _____

2. Class B Foam Concentrate (482) _____

   _____

3. Aqueous Film Forming Foam (AFFF) (483) _____

   _____

4. Alcohol-Resistant AFFF Concentrate (AR-AFFF) (484) _____

   _____

5. Drainage Time (485) _____

   _____

6. Expansion Ratio (485) _____

   _____

7. Bank-Down Application Method (Deflect) (486) _____

   _____

8. Rain-Down Method (486) _____

   _____

9. Roll-On Application Method (Bounce) (486) _____

   _____

10. Explosion-Proof Equipment (488) _____

_____

11. Dispersion (488) _____

_____

12. Dissolution (488) _____

_____

13. Containment (489) _____

_____

True/False

Write True or False on the blanks provided; if False, write the correct statement on the lines provided.

_____ 1. Neutralization is aimed at reducing or eliminating the chemical hazard of the material rather than physically containing it. (478)

_____

_____

_____ 2. Adsorption is different from absorption in that the molecules of the hazardous material physically adhere to the absorbent material rather than being absorbed into the inner spaces of an adsorbent material. (480)

_____

_____

_____ 3. Fluoroprotein foam has a very high degree of heat resistance and water retention. (484)

_____

_____

_____ 4. Emulsifiers work effectively with water-soluble or water-miscible fuels because an emulsion cannot be formed between the concentrate and the fuel. (485)

_____

_____

5. The roll-on method of foam application is when foam is sprayed into the air over the target area in a fog pattern. (486)

_____

_____

_____ 6. Dilution is often used during decontamination operations. (488)

_____

_____

_____ 7. Leak control and containment are generally considered defensive actions. (489)

_____

_____

_____ 8. When water streams are used to contain gas being released under pressure, the mass and velocity of the water streams must exceed the mass and velocity of the escaping gas. (494)

_____

_____

Matching

Write the correct answers on the blanks provided.

_____ 1. Physical and/or chemical event occurring during contact between materials with an attraction for each other (480)

_____ 2. Actions taken to control the flow of liquid hazardous materials away from the point of discharge (481)

_____ 3. Primarily used to control shallow liquid spills (480)

_____ 4. Action taken to reduce the emission of vapors at haz mat spill (482)

_____ 5. Prevents dispersion of materials such as powders or dusts (480)

A. Absorption
B. Adsorption
C. Blanketing/Covering
D. Dam, Dike, Diversion
E. Dilution
F. Dispersion
G. Dissolution
H. Neutralization
I. Vapor Dispersion
J. Vapor Suppression
K. Ventilation

_____ 6. Action taken to direct or influence the course of airborne hazardous materials (487)

_____ 7. Application of water to a water-soluble material to reduce the hazard (488)

_____ 8. Controlling the movement of air by natural or mechanical means (487)

_____ 9. Raising or lowering the pH of corrosive materials to render them neutral (488)

_____ 10. Breaking up or dispersing a hazardous material that has spilled on a solid or liquid surface (488)

_____ 11. Can only be used on water-soluble gases such as anhydrous ammonia (488)

A. Absorption

B. Adsorption

C. Blanketing/Covering

D. Dam, Dike, Diversion

E. Dilution

F. Dispersion

G. Dissolution

H. Neutralization

I. Vapor Dispersion

J. Vapor Suppression

K. Ventilation

Multiple Choice

Write the correct answers on the blanks provided.

_____ 1. Which of the following tactics are used to confine a hazardous material that has already been released from its container? (476)

A. Fire-control
B. Spill-control
C. Leak-control
D. Water-control

_____ 2. The main priority of spill control is: (477)

A. dilution.
B. ventilation.
C. confinement.
D. containment.

_____ 3. Which of the following is a defensive spill-control tactic to confine hazardous materials? (478)

A. Ventilation
B. Dispersion
C. Neutralization
D. Vapor suppression

_____ 4. Which of the following spill-control measures can be done with tarps, plastic sheeting, salvage covers, or other materials? (480)

A. Diversion
B. Adsorption
C. Vapor suppression
D. Blanketing/Covering

_____ 5. When actions are taken to control the flow of liquid hazardous materials away from the point of discharge, it is called: (481)

A. diversion.
B. adsorption.
C. vapor suppression.
D. blanketing/covering.

_____ 6. Which of the following foams maintains rather low viscosity at low temperatures? (484)

A. Fluoroprotein foam
B. Nonfluoroprotein foam
C. Class B foam concentrate
D. Aqueous Film Forming Foam (AFFF)

_____ 7. Which of the following is a characteristic of high-expansion foam concentrates? (485)

A. Compatible with dry-chemical extinguishing agents
B. Very high degree of heat resistance and water retention
C. Poor heat resistance because air-to-water ratio is very high
D. Fair penetrating capabilities in baled storage fuels or high surface-tension fuels

_____ 8. When foam deflects off the surface or object and flows down onto the surface of the spill, it is called the _____ method. (486)

A. rain-down
B. absorption
C. roll-on application
D. bank-down application

_____ 9. Which of the following rarely has practical applications at haz mat incidents in terms of spill control? (488)

A. Dilution
B. Dispersion
C. Dissolution
D. Neutralization

Crossword

Across

2 The amount of time it takes foam to break down or dissolve; also called drainage rate, drainage dropout rate, or drainage.

4 Act or process of being spread widely.

7 Encased in a rigidly built container so it withstands an internal explosion and also prevents ignition of a surrounding flammable atmosphere.

8 This method of foam application directs the stream into the air above the unignited or ignited spill or fire and allows the foam to float gently down onto the surface of the fuel.

9 Act of stopping the further release of a material from its container.

Down

1 Method of foam application in which the foam stream is directed at the ground at the front edge of the unignited or ignited liquid fuel spill.

3 Ratio of the finished foam volume to the volume of the original foam solution.

5 Act or process of dissolving one thing into another.

6 (1) Process of controlling the flow of a spill and capturing it at some specified location. (2) Operations required to prevent fire from extending from the area of origin to uninvolved areas or structures.

Skill Sheet 10-1

Objective 2: Perform absorption/adsorption. *[NFPA® 472, 6.6.4.1(3)(a)]*

Student Name: _____ Date: _____

Directions

For this skills evaluation checklist, students will perform the defensive control function of absorption/adsorption.

WARNING! Hazardous materials incidents can be extremely dangerous. Hazardous materials can cause serious injury or fatality. Appropriate personal protective equipment (PPE) must be worn and safety precautions must be followed. The following skill sheet demonstrates general steps; specific haz mat incidents may differ in procedure. Always follow departmental procedures for specific incidents.

Note: Prior to performing absorption/adsorption, the Incident Commander or other qualified responder must identify the material and determine the appropriate level of PPE required at the incident based on the hazardous material, training of responders, terrain, weather, and other size-up factors.

Equipment & Materials

- *Two first responders in full protective clothing*
- *A sorbent material*
- *A simulated hazardous materials liquid*
- *Shovels*
- *Trash hooks*
- *A secure container with lid*

Task Steps

1. Verify that all responders involved in the control function are wearing appropriate PPE for performing absorption/adsorption operations and that appropriate hand tools have been selected.
2. Select a location to efficiently and safely perform the absorption /adsorption operation.
3. Select the most appropriate sorbent/adsorbent.
4. Deploy the sorbent/adsorbent in a manner that most efficiently controls the spill.
5. Upon mitigation of the incident, place any contaminated material, such as clothing, in an approved container for transportation to a disposal location. Seal and label the container and document appropriate information for department records.
6. Decontaminate tools.
7. Advance to decontamination line for decontamination.

Skill Sheet 10-2

Objective 3: Perform damming operations. *[NFPA® 472, 6.6.4.1(3)(c)]*

Student Name: _____ **Date:** _____

Directions

For this skills evaluation checklist, students will perform the defensive control function of damming.

WARNING! Hazardous materials incidents can be extremely dangerous. Hazardous materials can cause serious injury or fatality. Appropriate personal protective equipment (PPE) must be worn and safety precautions must be followed. The following skill sheet demonstrates general steps; specific haz mat incidents may differ in procedure. Always follow departmental procedures for specific incidents.

Note: Prior to performing the defensive control function, the Incident Commander or other qualified responder must identify the material and determine the appropriate level of PPE required at the incident based on the hazardous material, training of responders, terrain, weather, and other size-up factors.

Equipment & Materials

- *Two first responders in full protective clothing*
- *Earth, sand, or rock*
- *A secure container with lid*
- *Shovels*
- *A simulated hazardous materials liquid*

Task Steps

1. Verify that all responders involved in the control function are wearing appropriate PPE for performing damming operations and that appropriate hand tools have been selected.
2. Select a location to efficiently and safely perform the damming operation.
3. Construct the dam in a location and manner that most efficiently controls the spill.
4. Upon mitigation of the incident, place any contaminated material, such as clothing, in an approved container for transportation to a disposal location. Seal and label the container and document appropriate information for department records.
5. Decontaminate tools.
6. Advance to decontamination line for decontamination.

Skill Sheet 10-3

Objective 4: Perform diking operations. *[NFPA® 472, 6.6.4.1(3)(d)]*

Student Name: _____ **Date:** _____

Directions

For this skills evaluation checklist, students will perform the defensive control function of diking.

WARNING! Hazardous materials incidents can be extremely dangerous. Hazardous materials can cause serious injury or fatality. Appropriate personal protective equipment (PPE) must be worn and safety precautions must be followed. The following skill sheet demonstrates general steps; specific haz mat incidents may differ in procedure. Always follow departmental procedures for specific incidents.

Note: Prior to performing the defensive control function, the Incident Commander or other qualified responder must identify the material and determine the appropriate level of PPE required at the incident based on the hazardous material, training of responders, terrain, weather, and other size-up factors.

Equipment & Materials

- *Two first responders in full protective clothing*
- *Earth, rock, or sand*
- *A secure container with lid*
- *Shovels*
- *A simulated hazardous materials liquid*

Task Steps

1. Verify that all responders involved in the control function are wearing appropriate PPE for performing diking operations and that appropriate hand tools have been selected.

2. Select a location to efficiently and safely perform the diking operation.

3. Construct the dike in a location and manner that most efficiently controls and directs the spill to a desired location.

4. Upon mitigation of the incident, place any contaminated material, such as clothing, in an approved container for transportation to a disposal location. Seal and label the container and document appropriate information for department records.

5. Decontaminate tools.

6. Advance to decontamination line for decontamination.

Skill Sheet 10-4

Objective 5: Perform diversion operations. *[NFPA® 472, 6.6.4.1(3)(f)]*

Student Name: _____ **Date:** _____

Directions

For this skills evaluation checklist, students will perform the defensive control function of diversion.

WARNING! Hazardous materials incidents can be extremely dangerous. Hazardous materials can cause serious injury or fatality. Appropriate personal protective equipment (PPE) must be worn and safety precautions must be followed. The following skill sheet demonstrates general steps; specific haz mat incidents may differ in procedure. Always follow departmental procedures for specific incidents.

Note: Prior to performing the defensive control function, the Incident Commander or other qualified responder must identify the material and determine the appropriate level of PPE required at the incident based on the hazardous material, training of responders, terrain, weather, and other size-up factors.

Equipment & Materials

- *Two first responders in full protective clothing*
- *Earth, rock, or sand*
- *A secure container with lid*
- *Tools, including shovels, picks, and wheelbarrows*
- *A simulated hazardous materials liquid*

Task Steps

1. Verify that all responders involved in the control function are wearing appropriate PPE for performing diversion operations and that appropriate hand tools have been selected.

2. Select a location to efficiently and safely perform the diversion operation.

3. Construct the diversion in a location and manner that most efficiently controls and directs the spill to a desired location. Working as a team, use hand tools to break the soil, remove the soil, pile the soil, and pack the soil tightly.

4. Upon mitigation of the incident, place any contaminated material, such as clothing, in an approved container for transportation to a disposal location. Seal and label the container and document appropriate information for department records.

5. Decontaminate tools.

6. Advance to decontamination line for decontamination.

Skill Sheet 10-5

Objective 6: Perform retention operations. *[NFPA® 472, 6.6.4.1(3)(g)]*

Student Name: _____ **Date:** _____

Directions

For this skills evaluation checklist, students will perform the defensive control function of retention.

WARNING! Hazardous materials incidents can be extremely dangerous. Hazardous materials can cause serious injury or fatality. Appropriate personal protective equipment (PPE) must be worn and safety precautions must be followed. The following skill sheet demonstrates general steps; specific haz mat incidents may differ in procedure. Always follow departmental procedures for specific incidents.

Note: Prior to performing the defensive control function, the Incident Commander or other qualified responder must identify the material and determine the appropriate level of PPE required at the incident based on the hazardous material, training of responders, terrain, weather, and other size-up factors.

Equipment & Materials

- *Two first responders in full protective clothing*
- *Tools, including shovels, picks, and wheelbarrows*
- *A simulated hazardous materials liquid*
- *A leaking simulated hazardous materials liquid vessel*
- *A secure container with lid*
- *A retention vessel*

Task Steps

1. Verify that all responders involved in the control function are wearing appropriate PPE for performing retention operations and that appropriate hand tools have been selected.

2. Select a location to efficiently and safely perform the retention operation.

3. Evaluate the rate of flow of the leak to determine the required capacity of the retention vessel.

4. Working as a team, retain the hazardous liquid so that it can no longer flow.

5. Upon mitigation of the incident, place any contaminated material, such as clothing, in an approved container for transport to a disposal location. Seal and label the container and document appropriate information for department records.

6. Decontaminate tools.

7. Advance to decontamination line for decontamination.

Skill Sheet 10-6

Objective 7: Perform vapor suppression. *[NFPA® 472, 6.6.4.1(3)(j)]*

Student Name: _____ **Date:** _____

Directions

For this skills evaluation checklist, students will perform vapor suppression by using fire-fighting foam.

WARNING! Hazardous materials incidents can be extremely dangerous. Hazardous materials can cause serious injury or fatality. Appropriate personal protective equipment (PPE) must be worn and safety precautions must be followed. The following skill sheet demonstrates general steps; specific haz mat incidents may differ in procedure. Always follow departmental procedures for specific incidents.

Note: Prior to performing the defensive control function, the Incident Commander or other qualified responder must identify the material and determine the appropriate level of PPE required at the incident based on the hazardous material, training of responders, terrain, weather, and other size-up factors.

Equipment & Materials

- *Two first responders in full protective clothing*
- *A pumping apparatus driver/operator*
- *A pumping apparatus*
- *Hoseline, foam nozzle, foam educator, foam*
- *A simulated hazardous materials liquid spill*
- *A simulated hazardous materials liquid vessel leaking a liquid*
- *A secure container with lid*
- *A reliable water source*

Task Steps

1. Ensure that all responders involved in control functions are wearing appropriate PPE for performing vapor suppression operations.
2. Select a location to efficiently and safely perform the vapor suppression operation.
3. Evaluate the quantity and surface area of the hazardous material that has leaked.
4. Determine the appropriate type of foam for the type of hazardous material present.
5. Working as a team, deploy the foam educator and foam, and advance the hoseline and foam nozzle to a position from which to apply the foam.
6. Flow hoseline until finished foam is produced at the nozzle.
7. Apply finished foam in an even layer convering the entire hazardous material spill area.

8. Upon mitigation of the incident, place any contaminated material in an approved container for transportation to a disposal location.

9. Seal, label, and manifest the container for removal.

10. Decontaminate tools.

11. Advance to decontamination line for decontamination.

Skill Sheet 10-7

Objective 8: Perform vapor dispersion. *[NFPA® 472, 6.6.4.1(3)(i)]*

Student Name: _____ **Date:** _____

Directions

For this skills evaluation checklist, students will perform the defensive control function of vapor dispersion.

WARNING! Hazardous materials incidents can be extremely dangerous. Hazardous materials can cause serious injury or fatality. Appropriate personal protective equipment (PPE) must be worn and safety precautions must be followed. The following skill sheet demonstrates general steps; specific haz mat incidents may differ in procedure. Always follow departmental procedures for specific incidents.

Note: Prior to performing the defensive control function, the Incident Commander or other qualified responder must identify the material and determine the appropriate level of PPE required at the incident based on the hazardous material, training of responders, terrain, weather, and other size-up factors.

Equipment & Materials

- *Two first responders in full protective clothing*
- *Atmospheric monitoring equipment*
- *A hoseline with attached fog nozzle*
- *A water source and pumping apparatus*
- *A simulated hazardous material vapor vessel*
- *A secure container with lid*
- *A pumping apparatus driver/operator*

Task Steps

1. Verify that all responders involved in the control function are wearing appropriate PPE for performing vapor dispersion operations.

2. Select a location to efficiently and safely perform the vapor dispersion operation.

3. Working as a team, advance the hoseline to a position to apply agent through vapor cloud to disperse vapors.

4. Constantly monitor the leak concentration, wind direction, exposed personnel, environmental impact, and water stream effectiveness.

5. Upon mitigation of the incident, place any contaminated material, such as clothing, in an approved container for transportation to a disposal location. Seal and label the container and document appropriate information for department records.

6. Decontaminate tools.

7. Advance to decontamination line for decontamination.

Skill Sheet 10-8

Objective 9: Perform dilution operations. *[NFPA® 472, 6.6.4.1(3)(e)]*

Student Name: _____ **Date:** _____

Directions

For this skills evaluation checklist, students will perform the defensive control function of dilution.

WARNING! Hazardous materials incidents can be extremely dangerous. Hazardous materials can cause serious injury or fatality. Appropriate personal protective equipment (PPE) must be worn and safety precautions must be followed. The following skill sheet demonstrates general steps; specific haz mat incidents may differ in procedure. Always follow departmental procedures for specific incidents.

Note: Prior to performing the defensive control function, the Incident Commander or other qualified responder must identify the material and determine the appropriate level of PPE required at the incident based on the hazardous material, training of responders, terrain, weather, and other size-up factors.

Equipment & Materials

- *Two first responders in full protective clothing*
- *A pumping apparatus driver/operator*
- *A pumping apparatus*
- *A simulated hazardous materials liquid nitric acid spill*
- *A simulated leaking hazardous materials liquid vessel*
- *Engine, hoselines, and water*
- *A secure container with lid*

Task Steps

1. Verify that all responders involved in the control function are wearing appropriate PPE for performing dilution operations.
2. Select a location to efficiently and safely perform dilution operations.
3. Evaluate the rate of flow of the leak to determine the required capacity of the retention area and the quantity of water required to dilute the material.
4. Working as a team, monitor and assess the leak, and advance hoselines and tools to retention area.
5. Flow water to dilute spilled material.
6. Monitor any diking or dams to ensure integrity of retention area.
7. Upon mitigation of the incident, place any contaminated material, such as clothing, in an approved container for transportation to a disposal location. Seal and label the container and document appropriate information for department records.

8. Decontaminate tools.

9. Advance to decontamination line for decontamination.

Skill Sheet 10-9

Objective 11: Perform remote valve shutoff. *[NFPA® 472, 6.6.4.1(3)(h)]*

Student Name: _____ **Date:** _____

Directions

For this skills evaluation checklist, students will perform remote valve shutoff at a fixed facility.

WARNING! Hazardous materials incidents can be extremely dangerous. Hazardous materials can cause serious injury or fatality. Appropriate personal protective equipment (PPE) must be worn and safety precautions must be followed. The following skill sheet demonstrates general steps; specific haz mat incidents may differ in procedure. Always follow departmental procedures for specific incidents.

Note: Prior to performing the defensive control function, the Incident Commander or other qualified responder must identify the material and determine the appropriate level of PPE required at the incident based on the hazardous material, training of responders, terrain, weather, and other size-up factors.

Equipment & Materials

* *Two first responders in full protective clothing*

Task Steps

1. Ensure that all responders involved in control functions are wearing appropriate PPE for performing remote valve shutoff operations.
2. Identify and locate the emergency remote shutoff device.
3. Operate the emergency remote shutoff device properly.
4. Notify the Incident Commander of the completed objective.
5. Document the activity log.

Chapter 11

Air Monitoring and Sampling

Terms

Write the definition of the terms below on the blanks provided.

1. Instrument Reaction Time (512) _____

   _____

2. Dose (514) _____

   _____

3. Concentration (514) _____

   _____

4. Calibration (519) _____

   _____

5. Ionization Potential (IP) (537) _____

   _____

6. Reagent (538) _____

   _____

7. Curie (Ci) (543) _____

   _____

8. Becquerel (Bq) (543) _____

   _____

9. International System of Units (Système International d'unités) (543) _____

   _____

11

10. Roentgen (R) (543) _____

_____

11. Roentgen Equivalent in Man (rem) (543) _____

_____

12. Radiation Absorbed Dose (rad) (543) _____

_____

13. Dosimeter (546) _____

_____

14. Infrared Thermometer (547) _____

_____

True/False

Write True or False on the blanks provided; if False, write the correct statement on the lines provided.

_____ 1. No one device or instrument will detect, identify, and measure all hazardous materials. (511)

_____

_____

_____ 2. An instrument's reaction or response time is the seconds taken to draw in a sample and analyze it. (512)

_____

_____

_____ 3. Monitoring and sampling results only need one sampling method and one technology. (513)

_____

_____

_____ 4. Concentration of a substance can be expressed through grams per kilogram (g/kg). (514)

_____

_____

5. While monitoring one should move quickly, making allowances for instruments with significant response times. (519)

_____

_____

6. Corrosive gases and vapors can damage detection and monitoring instruments as well as PPE. (524)

_____

_____

7. Fluoride test papers cannot be used to determine the presence of fluoride ions and gaseous hydrogen fluoride. (528)

_____

_____

8. Oxygen sensors last a long time, even when they are not in use. (529)

_____

_____

9. Flame ionization detectors (FIDs) should be operated in moderate temperatures. (540)

_____

_____

10. Raman spectrometers can cause a reaction in some reactive materials. (541)

_____

_____

11. An infrared thermometer is a monitor or device designed to detect reactive materials. (547)

_____

_____

11

Matching

Match the correct statement to each term.

_____ 1. Can vary from moderate (unable to see, breathless) to severe (convulsions) (533)

_____ 2. Lowest concentration of a gas or vapor capable of killing a specified species over a specified time (533)

_____ 3. Minimum concentration of an inhaled substance in the gaseous state that will be fatal to the test group (usually within 1 to 4 hours) (532)

_____ 4. Lowest administered dose of a material capable of killing a specified test species (532)

_____ 5. Statistically derived single dose of a substance that can be expected to cause death in 50 percent of animals when administered by the oral route (532)

_____ 6. Minimum amount of solid or liquid that when ingested, absorbed, or injected through the skin will cause death (532)

A. Incapacitating dose (ID)

B. Lethal concentration (LC)

C. Lethal concentration low (LCLO or LCL)

D. Lethal dose (LD)

E. Lethal dose low (LDLO or LDL)

F. Median lethal dose (LD_{50})

Matching

Match the correct statement to each term.

_____ 1. Measure the change in sensor conductivity using an electric circuit (550)

_____ 2. Indicate the presence of biological agents and toxins by detecting the presence of specific antibodies; most of these detectors require an active sample to be placed in the device in order to be analyzed (547)

_____ 3. Utilize various technologies to specifically detect chemical warfare agents; most require the responder to come in close contact with the material that is suspected to be a chemical agent (547)

HAZARDOUS MATERIALS FOR FIRST RESPONDERS COURSE WORKBOOK

_____ 4. Devices using infrared spectroscopy technology compare the infrared spectra of chemical samples against a library of known spectral signatures (548)

_____ 5. Use a highly sensitive microphone to essentially listen to the sound made when a material absorbs infrared radiation (548)

_____ 6. Include organic vapor badges (or film strips, wrist bands, stick pins, etc.), mercury badges, and formaldehyde badges or strips used to measure individual exposure to certain chemicals (550)

_____ 7. Utilize surface acoustical wave technology to detect nerve agents and blister agents (550)

_____ 8. Used to identify DNA; used to detect and identify biological agents and toxins (550)

_____ 9. Identify specific DNA sequences, thereby detecting and identifying types of biological agents (550)

_____ 10. Contain portable chemistry sets designed to enable logical and progressive testing of a sample in order to identify it (550)

_____ 11. Use a radioactive source to ionize samples in order to determine their spectra (549)

_____ 12. Chemical analysis instruments used to separate and identify chemicals in a complex sample (549)

_____ 13. Ionize samples to determine their composition (549)

A. Biological immunoassay indicators

B. Chemical agent monitors (CAMs)

C. DNA fluoroscopy devices

D. Fourier Transform Infrared (FTIR) spectrometers

E. Gas chromatography (CG) detectors

F. Ion-mobility spectrometers

G. Mass spectrometers

H. Photoacoustic IR spectroscopy (PIRS)

I. Polymerase chain reaction devices (PCRs)

J. Other personal detection devices

K. Surface acoustical wave devices (SAWs)

L. Thermoelectric Conductivity

M. Wet chemistry testing kits

11

Short Answer

Write the correct answers on the blanks provided.

1. Provide four tasks that air monitoring and sampling can assist in mitigation. (512)

   _____

   _____

   _____

   _____

2. List the keys to mitigation efforts in the hot zone that may require respiratory protection and chemical protective clothing. (520-521)

   _____

   _____

   _____

3. What are the three ways to measure the amount of flammable vapors and gases in the atmosphere? (530)

   _____

   _____

   _____

4. What questions should a monitoring plan take into consideration? (519)

   _____

   _____

   _____

   _____

   _____

5. What should a responder do if the self-reading dosimeter (SRD) reading is off-scale? (546)

   _____

   _____

   _____

   _____

Multiple Choice

Write the correct answers on the blanks provided.

_____ 1. Responders assigned detecting, monitoring, and sampling duties must be: (513)
   A. able to input the data provided to them.
   B. trained to correctly use the instruments available to them.
   C. trained to Technician-level in following predetermined procedures.
   D. able to select the correct device based on predetermined procedures.

_____ 2. To stay safe while monitoring, operate under the direction of a (an): (519)
   A. haz mat technician.
   B. fellow first responder.
   C. law enforcement officer.
   D. Awareness-Level responder.

_____ 3. Which of the following is NOT a factor related to monitoring instruments? (522)
   A. Training
   B. Calibration
   C. Concentration
   D. Instrument reaction time

_____ 4. Which of the following is a strong base for pH? (526)
   A. 0
   B. 7
   C. 9
   D. 10

_____ 5. All the following are limitations of pH paper EXCEPT: (527)
   A. need for close proximity with the hazardous material in order to conduct testing.
   B. strong oxidizers such as chlorine, bromine, and fluorine can cause high readings.
   C. difficulty reading the paper if the material is contaminated with opaque materials.
   D. difficulty reading the paper if the material chemically strips the paper in unexpected ways.

_____ 6. Normal air contains what percentage of oxygen? (528)
   A. 1
   B. 20.9
   C. 23.5
   D. 78.1

_____ 7. Which of the following is a limitation of combustible gas indicators (CGI) meters? (530)

    A. Meter response may be sluggish in extremely cold weather.

    B. Sensors deteriorate steadily over time, needing frequent replacement.

    C. Breathing into the CGI meter to test will blow carbon dioxide into the sensor, which causes degradation.

    D. Changes in temperature (and temperature extremes), humidity, and atmospheric pressure can affect the monitor.

_____ 8. When should a photoionization detector (PID) be used? (536)

    A Investigating complaints about noises

    B. Locating high-volume chemical releases

    C. At the edge of a release, where concentrations may be too high to be detected by a CGI

    D. When atmospheric contamination is suspected involving either flammable and/or non-flammable atmospheres

_____ 9. Which of the following are substances that are known to react with other chemicals in a specific way? (538)

    A. Reagents

    B. Reactions

    C. Directors

    D. Contractors

_____ 10. What devices are known to have a significant error rate of 25%-35%? (539)

    A. Flame ionization detectors

    B. Photoionization dectectors

    C. Chemical specific detectors

    D. Colorimetric indicator tubes

_____ 11. Which of the following devices will detect organic gases and vapors at low concentrations, but will NOT detect inorganic materials at all? (540)

    A. Raman spectrometers

    B. Photoionization detectors

    C. Flame ionization detectors

    D. Chemical specific detectors

_____ 12. Which of the following is starch paper that can be used to test the oxidizing potential of unknown chemicals? (542)

    A. Becquerels

    B. Potassium iodide (KI)

    C. Triacetone tiperoxide (TATP)

    D. Hexamethyline tiperoxide diamine (HMTD)

11

Across

3 A chemical that is known to react to another chemical or compound in a specific way, often used to detect or synthesize another chemical.

5 (1) Quantity of a chemical material inhaled for purposes of measuring toxicity. (2) Percentage (mass or volume) of a material dissolved in water (or other solvent).

6 Modern metric system, based on units of ten.

7 A non-contact measuring device that detects the infrared energy emitted by materials and converts the energy factor into a temperature reading.

Down

1 The energy required to free an electron from its atom or molecule.

2 Elapsed time between the movement of an air sample into a monitoring/detection device and the reading provided to the user.

4 English System unit used to measure the amount of radiation energy absorbed by a material.

5 Set of operations used to standardize or adjust the values of quantities indicated by a measuring instrument.

Skill Sheet 11-1

Objective 6: Perform a pH test on an unknown liquid. *[NFPA® 472, 6.7.4.1, 6.7.4.2]*

Student Name: _____ **Date:** _____

Directions

For this skills evaluation checklist, students will perform a pH test on an unknown liquid by correctly using pH paper.

WARNING! Hazardous materials incidents can be extremely dangerous. Hazardous materials can cause serious injury or fatality. Appropriate personal protective equipment (PPE) must be worn and safety precautions must be followed. The following skill sheet demonstrates general steps; specific haz mat incidents may differ in procedure. Always follow departmental procedures for specific incidents.

Note: Prior to performing monitoring and detection activities, the incident commander or other qualified responder must attempt to identify the hazardous material present and determine the appropriate level of PPE required at the incident based on the training of responders, terrain, weather, and other size-up factors. Operations-Level responders performing monitoring and detection activities must do so under the guidance of a haz mat technician, allied professional, or SOPs.

Equipment & Materials

- *pH paper*
- *Operational manual and color chart for pH paper*
- *Two responders in full protective clothing*
- *Pipettes*

Task Steps

1. Ensure that all responders are wearing appropriate PPE for performing testing operations.

2. Select appropriate monitor for specific situation.

3. Consider expiration date of pH papers. Prepare tape or strips for testing.

4. Approach the product from uphill and upwind. Make certain that no responders come in direct contact with the spilled product.

5. When approaching the product, determine the presence of corrosive vapors by waving wetted test paper in atmosphere.

6. If vapors do not exist, take sample of liquid product using a pipette without personally coming into contact with the material.

    Note: If necessary, attach strip to long rod or pole to ensure that user does not come into contact with material.

7. Compare results to pH paper chart to determine if the product is an acid, a base, or neutral.

Note: Confirmation of a corrosive atmosphere will eliminate the use of electronic meters for further testing.

8. Dispose of contaminated test paper accordingly.

9. Advance to decontamination line for decontamination.

Skill Sheet 11-2

Objective 7: Perform air monitoring with a multi-gas meter. *[NFPA® 472, 6.7.4.1, 6.7.4.2]*

Student Name: _____ **Date:** _____

Directions

For this skills evaluation checklist, students will perform air monitoring by correctly using a multi-gas meter.

WARNING! Hazardous materials incidents can be extremely dangerous. Hazardous materials can cause serious injury or fatality. Appropriate personal protective equipment (PPE) must be worn and safety precautions must be followed. The following skill sheet demonstrates general steps; specific haz mat incidents may differ in procedure. Always follow departmental procedures for specific incidents.

Note: Prior to performing monitoring and detection activities, the incident commander or other qualified responder must attempt to identify the hazardous material present and determine the appropriate level of PPE required at the incident based on the training of responders, terrain, weather, and other size-up factors. Operations-Level responders performing monitoring and detection activities must do so under the guidance of a haz mat technician, allied professional, or SOPs.

Equipment & Materials

- *Multi-gas meter*
- *Operational manual for multi-gas meter*
- *Two responders in full protective clothing*

Task Steps

1. Ensure that all responders are wearing appropriate PPE for performing testing operations.
2. Select appropriate monitor for specific situation. Note that electronic meters cannot be used in corrosive atmospheres.
3. Ensure that the multi-gas meter has been maintained and appropriately calibrated according to manufacturer's instructions.
4. Start up multi-gas meter and acquire a fresh-air calibration.
5. Approach the product from uphill and upwind. Before testing, consider the response time of multi-gas meter. Consider also the rising or sinking of particular materials in atmosphere. Responders should test atmosphere at various levels for appropriate readings.

   Note: Ensure that the meter remains a safe distance from the material at all times. If the meter is used to analyze a liquid, it must stay at least 1 inch (25 mm) away from product.

6. Approach the release and determine presence of:

   a. Flammable atmosphere (10% of LEL)

   Note: Responders using LEL meters must be aware that there are potential discrepancies in meter readings, and must make allowances to LEL readings accordingly (multipliers, response curves relative response, or correction factors).

   b. Oxygen-rich atmosphere (above 23.5%)

   c. Oxygen-deficient atmosphere (below 19.5%)

   d. Other toxic materials, depending on sensor (CO, H2S, NH3, PH3, etc.) being used

   Note: Be aware that some values may be read as percentage, while others may be read as ppm. Understand how your specific meter should be read.

7. If meter indicates an IDLH atmosphere, take appropriate actions according to AHJ.

8. Decontaminate meter according to manufacturer's instructions.

9. Advance to decontamination line for decontamination.

Skill Sheet 11-3

Objective 8: Perform air monitoring with a photoionization detector. *[NFPA® 472, 6.7.4.1, 6.7.4.2]*

Student Name: _____ **Date:** _____

Directions

For this skills evaluation checklist, students will perform air monitoring by correctly using a photoionization detector.

WARNING! Hazardous materials incidents can be extremely dangerous. Hazardous materials can cause serious injury or fatality. Appropriate personal protective equipment (PPE) must be worn and safety precautions must be followed. The following skill sheet demonstrates general steps; specific haz mat incidents may differ in procedure. Always follow departmental procedures for specific incidents.

Note: Prior to performing monitoring and detection activities, the incident commander or other qualified responder must attempt to identify the hazardous material present and determine the appropriate level of PPE required at the incident based on the training of responders, terrain, weather, and other size-up factors. Operations-Level responders performing monitoring and detection activities must do so under the guidance of a haz mat technician, allied professional, or SOPs.

Equipment & Materials

- *Photoionization detector*
- *Operational manual for photoionization detector*
- *Two responders in full protective clothing*

Task Steps

1. Ensure that all responders are wearing appropriate PPE for performing testing operations.

2. Select appropriate monitor for specific situation. Note that electronic meters cannot be used in corrosive atmospheres.

   Note: If material is known, determine ionization potential.

   Note: Determine electron volt strength of specific meter being used.

   Note: Determine if monitor reads in PPM or PPB.

3. Ensure that the photoionization detector has been maintained and appropriately calibrated according to manufacturer's instructions.

4. Start up PID meter and acquire a fresh-air calibration.

5. Approach the product from uphill and upwind. Before testing, consider the response time of the photoionization detector. Consider also the rising or sinking of particular materials in atmosphere. Responders should test atmosphere at various levels for appropriate readings.

Note: Ensure that the meter remains a safe distance from the material at all times. If the meter is used to analyze a liquid, it must stay at least 1 inch (25 mm) away from product.

6. Approach release and determine level of toxic gas or vapor in the atmosphere. Compare specific atmospheric levels according to established exposure values.

Note: Responders using PID meters must be aware that there are potential discrepancies in meter readings, and must make allowances to PID readings accordingly (multipliers, response curves relative response, or correction factors).

7. Decontaminate meter according to manufacturer's instructions.

8. Advance to decontamination line for decontamination.

Skill Sheet 11-4

Objective 9: Perform air monitoring with colorimetric indicator tubes. *[NFPA® 472, 6.7.4.1, 6.7.4.2]*

Student Name: _____ **Date:** _____

Directions

For this skills evaluation checklist, students will perform air monitoring by correctly using colorimetric indicator tubes.

WARNING! Hazardous materials incidents can be extremely dangerous. Hazardous materials can cause serious injury or fatality. Appropriate personal protective equipment (PPE) must be worn and safety precautions must be followed. The following skill sheet demonstrates general steps; specific haz mat incidents may differ in procedure. Always follow departmental procedures for specific incidents.

Note: Prior to performing monitoring and detection activities, the incident commander or other qualified responder must attempt to identify the hazardous material present and determine the appropriate level of PPE required at the incident based on the training of responders, terrain, weather, and other size-up factors. Operations-Level responders performing monitoring and detection activities must do so under the guidance of a haz mat technician, allied professional, or SOPs.

Equipment & Materials

- *Colorimetric unit (motorized pump, bellows, piston, or hand pump)*
- *Colorimetric tubes*
- *Operational manual for colorimetric unit*
- *Two responders in full protective clothing*

Task Steps

1. Ensure that all responders are wearing appropriate PPE for performing testing operations.

2. Ensure that tubes are within expiration dates.

3. If material is known, select appropriate tube. If material is unknown, use various clues at the scene to determine appropriate tube.

4. Consult manufacturer's instructions for specific applications and use of each tube.

5. Approach the product from uphill and upwind. Consider the rising or sinking of particular materials in atmosphere. Responders should test atmosphere at various levels for appropriate readings.

6. Break tips of both ends of tube and insert into colorimetric pump unit or insert colorimetric chip cartridge according to manufacturer's instructions. Perform testing of atmosphere.

   Note: Ensure that testing with individual tubes is performed in only ONE location. Movement during the testing process can result in skewed results.

7. Compare results to instructions provided by manufacturer.

   Note: It may be necessary to compare used tube to unused tube to verify that color change occurred.

8. Decontaminate according to manufacturer's recommendations. Dispose of used colorimetric tubes according to AHJ.

9. Advance to decontamination line for decontamination.

Skill Sheet 11-5

Objective 10: Detect radiation using a gas-filled detector. *[NFPA® 472, 6.7.4.1, 6.7.4.2]*

Student Name: _____ **Date:** _____

Directions

For this skills evaluation checklist, students will detect radiation by correctly using a gas-filled detector.

WARNING! Hazardous materials incidents can be extremely dangerous. Hazardous materials can cause serious injury or fatality. Appropriate personal protective equipment (PPE) must be worn and safety precautions must be followed. The following skill sheet demonstrates general steps; specific haz mat incidents may differ in procedure. Always follow departmental procedures for specific incidents.

Note: Prior to performing monitoring and detection activities, the incident commander or other qualified responder must attempt to identify the hazardous material present and determine the appropriate level of PPE required at the incident based on the training of responders, terrain, weather, and other size-up factors. Operations-Level responders performing monitoring and detection activities must do so under the guidance of a haz mat technician, allied professional, or SOPs.

Equipment & Materials

- *Gas-filled detector*
- *Operational manual for detector*
- *Two responders in full protective clothing*

Task Steps

1. Ensure that all responders are wearing appropriate PPE for performing testing operations.

2. Select the appropriate monitor for the specific situation.

3. Ensure that the detector has been maintained and appropriately calibrated according to manufacturer's instructions.

4. Start up the gas-filled meter and acquire background radiation levels (CPM for alpha and beta, or MREM for gamma).

5. Approach the product from uphill and upwind. Consider the rising or sinking of particular materials in atmosphere. Responders should test atmosphere at various levels for appropriate readings.

6. Read the meter accordingly.

   Note: Meters may read radiation using various terms. Understand how your specific meter reads radiation rates.

7. Determine the presence of gamma radiation.

   Note: Reading should be considered within the hot zone if it indicates two times above background.

8. Determine presence of alpha or beta radiation.

   Note: Reading should be considered within the hot zone if it indicates 200-300 CPM above background.

9. Compare radiation values to AHJ's SOP values to determine appropriate actions.

10. Decontaminate meter according to manufacturer's recommendations.

11. Advance to decontamination line for decontamination.

Chapter 12

Victim Rescue and Recovery

Write the definition of the terms below on the blanks provided.

1. Line of Sight (564) _____

   _____

2. Stokes Basket (576) _____

   _____

3. SKED® (577) _____

   _____

4. Recovery (579) _____

   _____

Write True or False on the blanks provided; if False, write the correct statement on the lines provided.

_____ 1. Bystander rescue has a low risk and low benefit. (567)

   _____

   _____

_____ 2. The primary factor in determining whether the environment is appropriate for structural PPE and SCBA is the viability of the victims. (567)

   _____

   _____

_____ 3. Upon completion of the extraction missions, first responders shall proceed through decontamination. (568)

   _____

   _____

_____ 4. The entry team must consist of no more than two trained members in the appropriate level of PPE. (573)

_____

_____

_____ 5. At haz mat incidents, rescuers typically start at the innermost part of the incident and work their way out. (573-574)

_____

_____

_____ 6. The last priority of rescuers is to recover the dead. (574)

_____

_____

_____ 7. It is always better to have two or more rescuers when attempting to move an adult. (577)

_____

_____

_____ 8. Recovery operations are a lower priority and should be coordinated by the Incident Commander with law enforcement or coroner personnel. (579)

_____

_____

Short Answer

Write the correct answers on the blanks provided.

1. For what must responders performing rescue and recovery operations be prepared for? (563-564)

_____

_____

_____

_____

_____

2. List the steps first responders should take prior to initiating rapid extraction. (568)

_____

_____

_____

_____

_____

3. Performing rescue and recovery operations requires which types of specialized tools and equipment? (576-577)

_____

_____

_____

_____

_____

_____

Multiple Choice

Write the correct answers on the blanks provided.

_____   1. First responders leave the rescue site, make appropriate notifications, and proceed to decontamination upon encountering which of the following exit conditions: (568)
   A. proceed to rehab, as needed.
   B. be guided by directions from the Hazardous Materials Task Force.
   C. any signs or symptoms of exposure for any members of an extraction team.
   D. PPE used during extraction should be kept segregated from other equipment until it is determined to be safe.

_____   2. Which of the following is NOT a basic question used to determine the feasibility of conducting rescue operations? (569-570)
   A. What products are involved?
   B. Are victims within line of sight or will a search be needed?
   C. Are there enough personnel available to conduct a rescue safely?
   D. Do on-scene emergency responders need the necessary equipment?

_____ 3. Which of the following is a responsibility of a unit leader? (572)

  A. Maintaining continuous communication during extraction efforts
  B. Establishing that there are viable victims and a need for extraction operations
  C Assigning someone else to designate team assignments and maintaining radio contact with members
  D. Continually maintaining both immediate and functional supervision over teams to ensure their safety during the operation

_____ 4. Which of the following victims are generally farthest from the release, have experienced the lowest exposure and related dose, and require the least amount of time to remove? (574)

  A. Line-of-Sight with Ambulatory
  B. Line-of-Sight with Non-Ambulatory
  C. Non-Line-of-Sight with Ambulatory
  D. Non-Line-of-Sight with Non-Ambulatory

_____ 5. Which of the following victims should be immediately directed to a safe haven or area of safe refuge where they can be assessed for decontamination need or medical treatment? (574)

  A. Line-of-Sight with Ambulatory
  B. Line-of-Sight with Non-Ambulatory
  C. Non-Line-of-Sight with Ambulatory
  D. Non-Line-of-Sight with Non-Ambulatory

_____ 6. Rescue and removal of which of the following victims typically poses the greatest danger to emergency response personnel and requires increased planning? (575)

  A. Line-of-Sight with Ambulatory
  B. Line-of-Sight with Non-Ambulatory
  C. Non-Line-of-Sight with Ambulatory
  D. Non-Line-of-Sight with Non-Ambulatory

_____ 7. Which triage priority includes victims that are seriously injured, but do not have life-threatening injuries? (576)

  A. Priority 1
  B. Priority 2
  C. Priority 3
  D. Priority 4

_____ 8. Which rescue method can be implemented by one rescuer using a loop of 1-inch (25 mm)? (578)

  A. Incline drag
  B. Seat/lift carry
  C. Webbing drag
  D. Three-person life/carry

_____ 9. Which rescue method is effective for carrying children or very small adults if they are conscious? (578)

    A. Incline drag
    B. Blanket drag
    C. Three-person lift/carry
    D. Cradle-in-arms lift/carry

_____ 10. Which carry provides more comfort for the victim in the supine position? (578)

    A. Seat lift
    B. Chair lift
    C. Extremities lift
    D. Three-person lift/carry

Skill Sheet 12-1

Objective 2: Conduct a triage. *[NFPA® 472, 6.8.4.1(4)]*

Student Name: _____ **Date:** _____

Directions

For this skills evaluation checklist, students will conduct triage.

Equipment & Materials

- *Simulated scene with multiple victims in various state of mobility, consciousness, and mental status.*

- *Triage tags*

Task Steps

1. Ensure scene safety and proper PPE.

2. Identify patients to be triaged.

3. Assess patient's mobility.

4. Assess patient's respiration.

   a. Attempt to open the airway. If breathing cannot be started by opening the airway, mark Priority 0.

   b. If patient starts breathing, or their respiratory rate is more than 30/minute, mark Priority 1.

   c. If respiratory rate is less than 30/minute, go to Step 5.

5. Assess patient's radial pulse.

   a. If patient is breathing, but has no radial pulse, mark Priority 1.

   b. If patient is breathing and has a pulse, go to Step 6.

6. Assess patient's level of consciousness.

   a. If patient is alert (able to follow simple commands), mark Priority 2.

   b. If any altered mental status, mark Priority 1.

7. Re-triage the Priority 3 "Walking Wounded" patients. Check for any change in medical condition, i.e. shock, mental status, etc.

Skill Sheet 12-2

Objective 5: Demonstrate the incline drag. *[NFPA® 472, 6.8.4.1(3)]*

Student Name: _____ **Date:** _____

Directions

For this skills evaluation checklist, students will demonstrate the incline drag. The incline drag is used by one rescuer to move a victim down a stairway or incline. It is very useful for moving an unconscious victim.

Equipment & Materials

* *Full protective clothing with SCBA*
* *Triage tags*

Task Steps

1. Turn the victim (if necessary) so that the victim is supine.
2. Kneel at the victim's head.
3. Support the victim's head and neck.

   Note: If head or neck injuries are suspected, provide appropriate support for head during movement.
4. Lift the victim's upper body into a sitting position.
5. Reach under the victim's arms.
6. Grasp the victim's wrists.
7. Stand. The victim can now be eased down a stairway or ramp to safety.

Skill Sheet 12-3

Objective 6: Demonstrate the blanket drag. *[NFPA® 472, 6.8.4.1(3)]*

Student Name: _____ **Date:** _____

Directions

For this skills evaluation checklist, students will demonstrate the blanket drag. The blanket drag is useful when a single firefighter is faced with moving a heavy victim. Rather than lifting the victim, the victim can be dragged on a blanket, rug, sheet, or similar object.

Equipment & Materials

- *Full protective clothing with SCBA*
- *Blanket, rug, or sheet*

Task Steps

1. Spread a blanket next to the victim, making sure that it extends above the victim's head.
2. Kneel on both knees at the victim's side opposite the blanket.
3. Extend the victim's nearside arm above his or her head.
4. Roll victim against your knees.
5. Pull the blanket against the victim, gathering it slightly against the victim's back.
6. Roll victim gently onto the blanket.
7. Straighten the blanket on both sides.
8. Wrap the blanket around the victim.
9. Tuck the lower ends around the victim's feet if enough blanket is available.
10. Pull the end of the blanket at the victim's head.
11. Drag the victim to safety.

Skill Sheet 12-4

Objective 7: Demonstrate the webbing drag. *[NFPA® 472, 6.8.4.1(3)]*

Student Name: _____ **Date:** _____

Directions

For this skills evaluation checklist, students will demonstrate the webbing drag.

Equipment & Materials

- *Full protective clothing with SCBA*
- *Webbing*

Task Steps

1. Place the victim on his or her back.
2. Slide the large webbing loop under victim's head and chest so the loop is even with their arm pits.
   a. Position the victim's arms so that they are outside the webbing.
   b. Form a large loop around the victim's torso at the chest level.
3. Pull the top of the large loop over the victim's head so that it is just past their head.
4. Reach down through the large loop and under the victim's back and grab the webbing.
5. Pull the webbing up and through the loop so that each webbing loop is drawn snugly around the victim's shoulders.
   a. Victim's arms next to the body
   b. Webbing placed high on shoulders close to the neck
6. Adjust hand placement on the webbing to support the victim's head.
   a. Move hands toward head to provide more support.
7. Drag the victim to safety by pulling on the webbing loop.

Skill Sheet 12-5

Objective 8: Demonstrate the cradle-in-arms lift/carry — One-rescuer method. *[NFPA® 472, 6.8.4.1(3)]*

Student Name: _____ **Date:** _____

Directions

For this skills evaluation checklist, students will demonstrate the cradle-in-arms lift/carry. This lift/carry is effective for carrying children or very small adults if they are conscious. It usually is not practical for carrying an unconscious adult because of the weight and relaxed condition of the body.

Equipment & Materials

* *Full protective clothing with SCBA*

Task Steps

1. Place one arm under the victim's arms and across the back.
2. Place the other arm under the victim's knees.
3. Lift the victim to about waist height.
   a. Keep your back straight (firefighter) while preparing to lift.
4. Carry the victim to safety.

Skill Sheet 12-6

Objective 9: Demonstrate the seat lift/carry — Two-rescuer method. *[NFPA® 472, 6.8.4.1(3)]*

Student Name: _____   **Date:** _____

Directions

For this skills evaluation checklist, students will demonstrate the seat/lift carry. The seat lift/carry can be used with a conscious or unconscious victim and is performed by two rescuers.

Equipment & Materials

* *Full protective clothing with SCBA*

Task Steps

1. Raise the victim to a sitting position.
2. Link arms across the victim's back.
3. Reach under the victim's knees to form a seat.
4. Lift the victim using your legs. Keep back straight while lifting.
5. Move the victim to safety.

Skill Sheet 12-7

Objective 10: Demonstrate the extremities lift/carry — Two-rescuer method. *[NFPA® 472, 6.8.4.1(3)]*

Student Name: _____   **Date:** _____

Directions

For this skills evaluation checklist, students will demonstrate the extremities lift/carry.

Equipment & Materials

* *Full protective clothing with SCBA*

Task Steps

1. Both Rescuers: Turn the victim (if necessary) so that the victim is supine. Keep head and neck stabilized during rolling to prevent spinal injury.

2. Rescuer #1: Kneel at the head of the victim.

3. Rescuer #2: Stand between the victim's knees.

4. Rescuer #1: Support the victim's head and neck with one hand and place the other hand under the victim's shoulders.

5. Rescuer #2: Grasp the victim's wrists.

6. Rescuer #2: Pull the victim to a sitting position.

7. Rescuer #1: Push gently on the victim's back.

8. Rescuer #1: Reach under the victim's arms and grasp the victim's wrists as Rescuer #2 releases them.

    a. Grasp the victim's left wrist with the right hand and right wrist with the left hand.

9. Rescuer #2: Turn around, kneel down, and slip hands under the victim's knees.

10. Both Rescuers: Stand and move the victim on command from Rescuer #1.

Skill Sheet 12-8

Objective 11: Demonstrate the chair lift/carry method 1 — Two rescuers. *[NFPA® 472, 6.8.4.1(3)]*

Student Name: _____ **Date:** _____

Directions

For this skills evaluation checklist, students will demonstrate the chair lift/carry. The chair lift/carry is used for either a conscious or an unconscious person. Inform students of the importance of using a sturdy chair. Remind them that this carry should NOT be attempted using a folding chair.

Equipment & Materials

- *Full protective clothing with SCBA*
- *Chair*

Task Steps

1. Both Rescuers: Turn the victim (if necessary) so that the victim is supine. Keep head and neck stabilized during rolling to prevent spinal injury.

2. Rescuer #1: Lift the victim's knees until the knees, buttocks, and lower back are high enough to slide a chair under the victim.

3. Rescuer #2: Slip a chair under the victim.

4. Both Rescuers: Raise the victim and chair to a 45-degree angle.

5. Both Rescuers: Lift the seated victim with one rescuer carrying the legs of the chair and the other carrying the back of the chair.

Skill Sheet 12-9

Objective 12: Demonstrate the chair lift/carry method 2 — Two rescuers. *[NFPA® 472, 6.8.4.1(3)]*

Student Name: _____   **Date:** _____

Directions

For this skills evaluation checklist, students will demonstrate the chair lift/carry. The chair lift/carry is used for either a conscious or an unconscious person. Inform students of the importance of using a sturdy chair. Remind them that this carry should NOT be attempted using a folding chair.

Equipment & Materials

- *Full protective clothing with SCBA*
- *Chair*

Task Steps

1. Rescuer #1: Place the victim in a sitting position.

2. Rescuer #1: Reach under the victim's arms and grasp the victim's wrists.

3. Rescuer #2: Position the chair next to the victim.

4. Rescuer #2: Grasp the victim's legs under the knees.

5. Both Rescuers: Lift gently and place the victim onto the chair.

6. Both Rescuers: Raise the victim and chair to a 45-degree angle.

7. Both Rescuers: Lift the seated victim with one rescuer carrying the legs of the chair and the other carrying the back of the chair.

Chapter 13

Evidence Preservation and Sampling

Write the definition of the terms below on the blanks provided.

1. Forensic Science (593) _____

    _____

2. Prosecute (601) _____

    _____

3. Warrant (601) _____

    _____

4. Search Warrant (601) _____

    _____

5. Affidavit (601) _____

    _____

6. Charge (601) _____

    _____

7. Documentation (602) _____

    _____

8. Case File (602) _____

    _____

9. Trace Evidence (604) _____

    _____

10. Transient Evidence (604) _____

    _____

11. Witness (603) _____

_____

12. Walk-Through (604) _____

_____

13. Chain of Custody (609) _____

_____

14. Case Identifiers (609) _____

_____

15. Site Characterization (610) _____

_____

16. Wipe Sample (612) _____

_____

17. Volatile Organic Compounds (VOCs) (615) _____

_____

True/False

Write True or False on the blanks provided; if False, write the correct statement on the lines provided.

_____   1. Illicit labs that generate illegal drugs are run by people who have a vested interest in maintaining their livelihood. (594)

_____

_____

_____   2. If a package is thought to be suspicious, responders should contact bomb squad personnel to investigate further. (594)

_____

_____

_____ 3. No more than one agency will be involved in an investigation. (596)

_____

_____

_____ 4. Reports pertaining to the crime scene investigation shall be compiled into documentation by the investigator(s) in charge of the crime scene. (602)

_____

_____

_____ 5. If bystanders are witnesses, they should be removed from the scene. (603)

_____

_____

_____ 6. During a scene walk-through, investigators should identify and protect fragile and perishable evidence. (605)

_____

_____

_____ 7. When evaluating evidence possibilities, investigators should move from most intrusive to least intrusive processing/collection methods. (605)

_____

_____

_____ 8. Sketches document evidence prior to movement. (606)

_____

_____

_____ 9. If evidence is locked in a vehicle, it does not need to be documented. (610)

_____

_____

_____ 10. A primary sampler is the same as a dirty sampler. (611)

_____

_____

_____ 11. Continue to use any sampling equipment that touches a non-sterile surface other than the sample itself. (616)

_____

_____

_____ 12. When performing the final survey, investigators will release the scene to the owner or responsible party. (617)

_____

_____

Matching

Match the appropriate statement with each FBI twelve-step process. (600)

_____ 1. Approach the Scene

_____ 2. Collect Evidence

_____ 3. Conduct Detailed Search

_____ 4. Evaluate Evidence Possibilities

_____ 5. Make Preparations

_____ 6. Perform a Preliminary Survey

_____ 7. Perform the Final Survey

_____ 8. Photograph the Scene

_____ 9. Prepare a Narrative Description

_____ 10. Prepare Diagrams and Sketches

_____ 11. Release the Crime Scene

_____ 12. Secure and Protect the Scene

A. Step 1
B. Step 2
C. Step 3
D. Step 4
E. Step 5
F. Step 6
G. Step 7
H. Step 8
I. Step 9
J. Step 10
K. Step 11
L. Step 12

Short Answer

Write the correct answers on the blanks provided.

1. What are the steps for the proper care of evidence when using the simple scientific and legal rules (SOPs)? (600)

   _____

   _____

   _____

   _____

   _____

   _____

   _____

   _____

   _____

   _____

2. What should haz mat monitoring teams be prepared to monitor for? (610)

   _____

   _____

   _____

   _____

3. At a minimum, for what do field screen samples test? (614-615)

   _____

   _____

   _____

   _____

   _____

13

Multiple Choice

Write the correct answers on the blanks provided.

_____ 1. Responders can achieve the goals of preserving life, stabilizing the incident, and obtaining _____ by carrying out duties as planned. (593)
   A. case files
   B. case identifiers
   C. forensic evidence
   D. site characterization

_____ 2. During the assessment of a suspicious package, which of the following questions should be answered? (595)
   A. Is the package silent?
   B. Is the package closed?
   C. Is there anything protruding?
   D. Is anyone who touched the package feeling ill?

_____ 3. Explosives, biological toxins, and toxic industrial chemicals are items that are used in: (594)
   A. illicit laboratories.
   B. environmental crimes.
   C. suspicious letters or packages.
   D. weapon of mass destruction attacks.

_____ 4. Which of the following can include additional hazards in the form of armed owners/operators? (594)
   A. Illicit laboratories
   B. Environmental crimes
   C. Suspicious letters or packages
   D. Weapon of mass destruction attacks

_____ 5. Which of the following response phases is accomplished when life safety objectives are met and the scene is stabilized and secured? (598)
   A. Tactical
   B. Criminal
   C. Operational
   D. Remediation

6. Responders at a WMD incident should: (599)
    A. limit the number of personnel into the scene and record their names.
    B. take samples with the intent of giving them to the appropriate law enforcement authority as evidence.
    C. linger in the site once public safety issues are addressed unless requested by law enforcement.
    D. attempt to process a WMD crime scene without contacting (or receiving approval from) the appropriate law enforcement authority.

7. During the preparation stage, applicable warrants and ___ must be obtained. (601)
    A. charges
    B. case files
    C. affidavits
    D. documentation

8. Which of the following statements about approaching a scene is MOST accurate? (602)
    A. Notes are not needed during the initial observations.
    B. The safety of the personnel is not of primary concern.
    C. Warrants or consent forms are not required upon arrival.
    D. Necessary PPE will be determined by the hazards at the scene.

9. Hair, textile fibers, paint chips, and glass fragments are examples of: (604)
    A. case files.
    B. trace evidence.
    C. documentation.
    D. transient evidence.

10. Which of the following should investigators do when collecting evidence? (608)
    A. Avoid chain of custody.
    B. Clear out each item identified.
    C. Leave items collected as evidence in clear sight.
    D. Avoid excessive handling of evidence after it is collected.

11. When should site characterization occur? (610)
    A. After determining a sampling plan
    B. While determining a sampling plan
    C. Before determining a sampling plan
    D. Never while determining a sampling plan

12. Sample plans should include sampling protocols for all the following EXCEPT: (610)
    A. field screening samples.
    B. labeling and packaging.
    C. replacing paper or glass fiber filters.
    D. decontaminating samples of evidence.

_____ 13. Which of the following samples would be used when contaminants are visible or suspected on surfaces? (612)

    A. Wipe
    B. Solid
    C. Label
    D. Liquid

_____ 14. Which of the following samples would require syringes and tubing? (613)

    A. Wipe
    B. Solid
    C. Label
    D. Liquid

13

Crossword

Across

1 A process used to maintain and document the chronological history of the evidence.

7 To charge someone with a crime; a prosecutor tries a criminal case on behalf of the government.

9 The alphabetic and/or numeric characters assigned to identify a particular case.

10 Application of scientific procedures to the interpretation of physical events such as those that occur at a fire scene.

11 A writ (written order) issued by a competent magistrate (or judge) authorizing an officer to make an arrest, a seizure, or a search or to do other acts incident to the administration of justice.

Down

2 The law that the law enforcement agency believes the defendant has broken.

3 The collection of documents comprising information concerning a particular investigation.

4 Written notes, audio/videotapes, printed forms, sketches and/or photographs that form a detailed record of the scene, evidence recovered, and actions taken during the search of the crime scene.

5 Physical evidence that results from the transfer of small quantities of materials.

6 Sample collected by wiping a representative surface of a known area.

8 Written statement of facts confirmed by the oath of the party making it, before a notary or officer having authority to administer oaths.

Skill Sheet 13-1

Objective 5: Demonstrate evidence preservation and sampling. *[NFPA® 472, 6.5.4.1(1-14)]*

Student Name: _____ **Date:** _____

Directions

For this skills evaluation checklist, students will preserve evidence and take samples of a hazardous material.

Equipment & Materials

- *Appropriate PPE*
- *Evidence collection kit*
- *Clip board and pens*
- *Monitoring and detection devices*
- *Cameras (video or still)*
- *Chain-of-custody forms*
- *Maps and diagrams*
- *Site entry log*

Task Steps

1. Prepare an evidence collection plan and evidence collection kit for use.
2. Follow all safety procedures to ensure safe entry into hot zone.
3. Ensure that all responders involved in evidence collection are wearing appropriate PPE for performing evidence collection operations in the hot zone.
4. Document all personnel entering hot zone to ensure proper documentation for chain of custody purposes.
5. Enter the scene. Document evidence using photography, sketches, and/or video as determined by the AHJ's SOPs.
6. Collect sample and prepare for field screening of corrosivity, flammability, oxidation, radioactivity, and volatile organic compounds, following AHJ's SOPs for evidence sampling and field screening.

   Note: Field screening for explosives or materials that can cause violent or toxic reactions should be conducted by bomb squad personnel. If explosives are found, withdraw and follow bomb squad instructions on how to proceed.

7. Seal sample container with tamper-proof seal. Label the seal with date, time, and initials/name of person collecting sample. Document sample location through photograph and/or written documentation.

8. Put sample into secondary container, such as zip-top bag. Label secondary container.

9. Proceed to decontamination line for decontamination.

10. Decontaminate exterior of secondary container while proceeding through decontamination.

Note: If any evidence changes custody during decontamination, this must be documented on chain of custody form.

Chapter 14

Illicit Laboratories

Terms

Write the definition of the terms below on the blanks provided.

1. Methamphetamine (Meth) (627) _____

   _____

2. Phosphine (628) _____

   _____

3. Organophosphate Pesticides (636) _____

   _____

4. Autoclave (641) _____

   _____

5. Glovebox (640) _____

   _____

6. Remediation (646) _____

   _____

True/False

Write True or False on the blanks provided; if False, write the correct statement on the lines provided.

_____ 1. An action to avoid booby traps is not to use explosion-proof equipment. (625)

   _____

   _____

2. It is estimated that for every pound (0.5 kg) of meth produced, 6 pounds (3 kg) of hazardous waste is generated. (635)

_____

_____

3. Drug labs are the second most common type of lab discovered, after explosive labs. (636)

_____

_____

4. Chemical and biological hazards are typically the same. (642)

_____

_____

5. Remediation is the act of fixing or correcting a fault, error, or deficiency. (646)

_____

_____

6. Assistance and information relating to remediation of illicit drug/WMD scenes should come from local and state health departments. (646)

_____

_____

Short Answer

Write the correct answers on the blanks provided.

1. With what crime scene jurisdictions and procedures should Operations Level responders be familiar? (644)

_____

_____

_____

_____

_____

_____

_____

2. Decontamination for tactical scenarios should be based upon a rapid deployment and anticipating what four potential sources requiring decontamination? (645)

_____

_____

_____

_____

Multiple Choice

Write the correct answers on the blanks provided.

_____   1. Which of the following is a task an illicit lab operator may do? (627)
     A. Legally dispose of hazardous waste
     B. Release hazardous vapors into residential areas
     C. Utilize proper approved processes and locations
     D. Pour nonhazardous waste down sanitary sewers

_____   2. What is sometimes classified as a chemical warfare choking agent? (628)
     A. Phosphine gas
     B. Pseudoephedrine
     C. Methamphetamine
     D. Organophosphate pesticides

_____   3. Which of the following are a sign of a meth lab? (635)
     A. Increased daytime activity
     B. Strong odor of solvents
     C. Windows are open and clear
     D. No discolored pavement or structures

_____   4. Which of the following are NOT an ingredient that may be found in peroxide-based explosive labs? (638)
     A. Alcohol
     B. Acetone
     C. Ethanol
     D. Hexamine

_____   5. Which of the following are biological labs MOST likely to contain? (639)
     A. Propane
     B. Gasoline
     C. Antibiotics
     D. Anhydrous ammonia

6. Which of the following is an indicator of a biological laboratory? (639-641)

    A. Normal ventilation system
    B. Chemicals such as gasoline and propane
    C. Bleach or other sterilization supplies such as antiseptics and autoclaves
    D. Instruction manuals or other books, magazines, and internet resources relating to drug agents

7. Which of the following is NOT used to sterilize objects? (641)

    A. Bleach
    B. Glovebox
    C. Autoclave
    D. Antiseptic

8. Which of the following is a coordination challenge that may comprise more than one entity? (642)

    A. Neutralizing tactical threats
    B. Rendering safe any explosive ordnance or booby traps
    C. Protecting evidence from potential damage or destruction
    D. Determining atmospheric hazards through air monitoring/detection

9. Which of the following are monitoring and detection equipment? (643)

    A. Grinders
    B. Heat sources
    C. Oxygen meters
    D. Condenser tubes

10. PPE selection is based upon the assessment of all the following EXCEPT: (645)

    A. outward warning signs.
    B. decontamination procedures.
    C. intelligence about laboratory operations and contents.
    D. detection clues such as any protective clothing used by the operator, activity of animals in the laboratory, interviews with neighbors.

Crossword

Across

4 A device that uses high-pressure steam to sterilize objects.

5 Act of fixing or correcting a fault, error, or deficiency.

Down

1 A central nervous system stimulant drug that is similar in structure to amphetamine.

2 A colorless, flammable, and toxic gas with an odor of garlic or decaying fish which can ignite spontaneously on contact with air

3 A sealed container designed to allow a trained scientist to manipulate microorganisms

Skill Sheet 14-1

Objective 2: Identify and avoid booby traps at illicit laboratories. *[NFPA® 472, 6.9.4.1.1(3)]*

Student Name: _____ **Date:** _____

Directions
For this skills evaluation checklist, students will identify and avoid booby traps, trigger wires, and other suspicious items at illicit laboratories.

Equipment & Materials
- *Two responders in appropriate PPE*
- *Flashlight*
- *Mirror device on long handle*
- *Air Monitoring*
- *Temperature gun*
- *Thermal camera*
- *IR camera*
- *Bombsuit (optional)*

Task Steps

1. Upon suspicion of an illicit lab, notify bomb squad of possible response.
2. Make preparations for safe entry, including appropriate PPE and correct safety procedures.
3. Maintain situational awareness at all times.
4. Approach the scene carefully, looking for anything suspicious or unusual.
5. Before opening doors or windows, examine for any signs of tampering or booby traps. Start low and work upwards, looking for wires, trigger devices, or items that may fall upon opening.
6. If nothing is found, open door slowly and carefully. Proceed cautiously into room.
7. Upon entering, do not touch or change the environment in any way. This includes but is not limited to turning lights or HVAC units on or off or turning electricity to building off.
8. Examine the room in sections; floor to waist, waist to chin, chin to ceiling, and false ceilings if applicable. Look for wires, bottles, pipes, trip wires, or anything out of the ordinary or that arouses your curiosity.
9. If any suspicious items are noticed, back out of the area, retracing your footsteps. Contact the bomb squad immediately.
10. Upon their arrival, brief bomb squad personnel on findings.
11. Follow bomb squad instructions for proceeding.

Notes

Notes